O, beware, my lord, of jealousy!
It is the green-eyed monster which doth mock
The meat it feeds on.

THE TRAGEDY OF OTHELLO
Act III, Scene 3

THE TRAGEDY OF OTHELLO

THE MOOR OF VENICE

William Shakespeare

with Connections

HOLT, RINEHART AND **WINSTON**
Harcourt Brace & Company

Austin • New York • Orlando • Atlanta • San Francisco
Boston • Dallas • Toronto • London

**For permission to reprint copyrighted material, grateful
acknowledgment is made to the following sources:**

**Bantam Books, a division of Bantam Doubleday Dell Publishing
Group, Inc.:** From "Introduction" (retitled "Self-knowledge at a Terrible
Price") by David Bevington from *Othello* by William Shakespeare, edited by
David Bevington. Introduction copyright © 1988 by David Bevington.
The Estate of Mark Van Doren: From "Othello" (retitled "The Tragedy of
Othello") from *Shakespeare* by Mark Van Doren. Copyright © 1939 and
renewed © 1967 by Mark Van Doren.
Roxana Tynan and Wheelshare Limited: From "Laurence Olivier with
Kenneth Tynan" (retitled "On Playing Othello: Sir Laurence Olivier
Interviewed by Kenneth Tynan") by Kenneth Tynan from *Great Acting,*
edited by Hal Burton. Copyright © 1967 by Kenneth Tynan and British
Broadcasting Corporation.
The New York Times Company: "After Four Centuries, Shakespeare
Comes to Life in His Natural Habitat" by Alan Riding from *The New York
Times,* June 12, 1997. Copyright © 1997 by The New York Times Company.

Cover art: Joe Melomo, Design Director; Shoehorn, Inc., Designer; Andrew
Yates, Photographer; Mike Gobbi, Photo Researcher

HRW is a trademark licensed to Holt, Rinehart and Winston, registered in
the United States of America and/or other jurisdictions.

Printed in the United States of America

ISBN 0-03-057302-5   3 4 5 6 043 03 02 01

CONTENTS

The Renaissance Theater

Drama as Teacher: The Forerunners

Even before the Renaissance, the English had been writing and performing plays for several centuries. Some scholars believe that medieval drama evolved from church ceremonies such as the dialogue songs performed at Easter Eve services. In these tiny playlets three women would appear at a door representing the tomb of Christ and guarded by an angel. The angel would ask in Latin, "Whom do you seek?" and then he would announce the Resurrection.

From this obscure beginning, drama moved out of the churches and into the marketplaces of towns. There, in the 1300s and 1400s, various workers' guilds cooperated in staging cycles of plays that dramatized the whole history of the human race as then understood: its creation by God, its fall through the wiles of Satan, its life in Old Testament times, its redemption by Christ, and its final judgment at the end of the world. Parts of four cycles of these plays have been preserved, and they are named after the towns where they probably originated: York, Chester, Coventry, and Wakefield. Gradually the plays became less religious, often relying on *deus ex machina* (an artificial device arbitrarily used to resolve a plot), and comedy was incorporated into them. The wife of Noah, for instance, makes a great fuss about entering the ark and is carried kicking and screaming aboard. Comic scenes like this one provide an early example of English skill in mixing the comic with the serious in drama. The most notable play of the period just before the Renaissance is *Everyman,* based on a Dutch original.

Several kinds of plays, then, were written and produced before the Renaissance: **miracle** and **mystery plays,** which taught people stories from the Bible and legends of saints; **moralities,** which taught people how to live and die; and, starting in the early 1500s, a new kind of play called an **interlude.** Interludes were one-act plays, some of them indistinguishable from moralities, others rowdy and farcical. With the interludes the playwrights stopped being anonymous. Even before the new humanist learning came in, there were strong dramatic traditions that the great Renaissance playwrights knew about.

Old Traditions, New Theaters

By the mid–sixteenth century, the art of drama in England was three centuries old, but the idea of housing it in a permanent building was new. Even after theaters were built, plays were still regularly performed in improvised spaces when acting companies toured the provinces or presented their plays in the large houses of royalty and nobility.

In 1576, James Burbage, the father of Shakespeare's partner and fellow actor Richard Burbage, built the first public theater and called it, appropriately, the Theater. Shortly thereafter a second playhouse, called the Curtain, was erected. Both of these were in a northern suburb of London, where they would not offend the staid residents of London proper. Then came the Rose, the Swan, the Fortune, the Globe, the Red Bull, and the Hope—far more public theaters than in and around any other European capital.

The Globe: "This Wooden O"

The Globe is the most famous of the public theaters because Shakespeare's company owned it. Many of his plays received their first performances there. It was built out of timber salvaged from the Theater, which was demolished in 1599. Unfortunately, the plans for the Globe have not survived, though there still exist old panoramic drawings of London in which its exterior is pictured. But the most important sources of information about the theater's structure are the plays themselves, with their stage directions and other clues.

Most scholars now accept as accurate the reconstruction of the Globe published by C. Walter Hodges. The theater had three main parts: the building proper, the stage, and the tiring house, or backstage area. A flag flying from its peak indicated there would be a performance that day.

A wooden structure three stories high, the building proper surrounded a spacious inner yard open to the sky. It was probably a sixteen-sided polygon. Any structure with that many sides would appear circular, so it is not surprising that Shakespeare referred to the Globe as "this wooden O" in his play *Henry V*. There were probably only two entrances to the building, one for the public and one for the theater company. But there may have been another public door used as an exit, because when the Globe burned down in 1613, the crowd escaped quickly and safely.

General admission to the theater cost one penny; this entitled a spectator to be a groundling, which meant he or she could stand in the yard. Patrons paid a little more to enter the galleries, where there were seats and a better view of the stage. The most expensive seats were chairs set along two sides of the stage. People who wanted to be conspicuous rented them, though they must have been a great nuisance to the rest of the audience and the actors. A public theater held a surprisingly large number of spectators—three thousand, according to two contemporary accounts. Since the spectators must have been squeezed together, it is no wonder that the authorities closed the theaters during epidemics of the plague. (In 1996 a new Globe, closely modeled on Shakespeare's Globe, was opened in London, near the theater's original location. It, too, is built mainly of wood, with a thatched roof. The stage and galleries are covered, but the inner space for groundlings is unprotected from stormy skies, just as in Shakespeare's day.)

Up Close and Personal

The stage jutted halfway out into the yard, so that the actors were in much closer contact with the audience than actors are in modern theaters. Thus, every tiny nuance of an actor's perform-ance could affect the audience. The actors were highly trained, and they could sing, dance, declaim, wrestle, fence, clown, roar, weep, and whisper. Large, sensational effects were also plentiful. Spectators loved to see witches or devils emerge through the trapdoor in the stage, which everybody pretended led down to hell, just as everybody pretended that the ceiling over part of the stage was the heavens. This ceiling was painted with elaborate suns, moons, and stars, and it contained a trapdoor through which angels, gods, and spirits could be lowered on a wire and even flown over the other actors' heads.

Behind the Scenes

The third part of the theater was the tiring (from *tire,* an archaic form of *attire*) house, a tall building that contained machinery and dressing rooms and that provided a two-story back wall for the stage. Hodges's drawing of the Globe shows that this wall contained a gallery above and a curtained space below. The gallery had multiple purposes, depending on what play was being performed: Spectators could sit there, musicians could perform there, or parts of the play could be acted there—as if on balconies, towers, hills, and the like. The curtained area below the gallery was used mainly for "discoveries" of things prepared in advance and hidden from the audience until the proper time. In Shakespeare's *Merchant of Venice,* for example, the curtain is drawn to reveal three small chests, one of which hides the hero-ine's picture. Apparently this curtained area was too small, too shallow, and too far out of the sight of some spectators to be used as a performance space. If a performer were "discovered" behind the curtains (as Marlowe's Dr. Faustus is discovered in his study), he would quickly move out onto the stage to be seen and heard better. When large properties such as thrones, beds, desks, and so on were pushed through the curtains onto the stage, the audience would know at once that the action was taking place indoors. When the action shifted to the outdoors, the property could be pulled back behind the curtain.

The Power of Make-Believe

Renaissance audiences took for granted that the theater cannot show reality: Whatever happens on the stage is make-believe. When the people in the audience saw actors carrying lanterns, they accepted that it was night, even though the sun was shining brightly overhead. Often, instead of seeing a scene, they heard it described, as when Shakespeare has a character exclaim over a sunrise,

> But look, the morn in russet mantle clad
> Walks o'er the dew of yon high eastward hill.
> —*Hamlet,* Act I, Scene 1

When a forest setting was called for, there was no painted scenery imitating real trees, bushes, flowers, and so on. Instead, a few bushes and small trees might be pushed onto the stage, and then the actors spoke lines that evoked images in the spectators' minds. In *As You Like It,* Rosalind simply looks around and announces, "Well, this is the forest of Arden." As the theater historian Gerald Bentley put it, Renaissance drama was "a drama of persons, not a drama of places."

Pomp and Pageantry

The scenery may have been kept to a minimum, but the theaters themselves in Renaissance England were ornate. The interiors were painted brightly, with many decorations, and the space at the rear of the stage could be covered with colorful tapestries or hangings. Costumes were rich, elaborate, and expensive. The manager-producer Philip Henslowe once paid twenty pounds (then an enormous sum) for a single cloak for one of his actors to wear. Henslowe's lists of theatrical properties mention chariots, fountains, dragons, beds, tents, thrones, booths, and wayside crosses, among other things.

The audience also enjoyed the processions—religious, royal, military—that occurred in many plays. These would enter the stage from one door, cross the stage, and then exit by the other door. A few quick costume changes as the actors passed through the tiring house could double and triple the apparent number of people in a procession.

Music Most Eloquent

When people went to the London theater, they expected not only to see a tragedy or comedy acted but also to hear music, both vocal and instrumental. Trumpets announced the beginning of the play and important arrivals and departures within the play. High up in the gallery, musicians played between acts and at appropriate times during the performance. Songs were scattered throughout most of the plays, especially the comedies.

The songs in Shakespeare's plays are the best of this kind that have come down to us, for Shakespeare excelled in lyric and in dramatic poetry. He included a great variety of songs in his plays: sad, happy, comic, thoughtful songs, each one closely related to the play in which it occurs and to the character who performs it. Some of the songs advance the dramatic action, some help establish mood, and some reveal character. Like this invitation to love (from the comedy *Twelfth Night*), the songs are fresh and spontaneous, not contrived and artificial.

O mistress mine, where are you roaming?
O, stay and hear, your true love's coming,
    That can sing both high and low.

Trip no further, pretty sweeting;
Journeys end in lovers meeting,
   Every wise man's son doth know . . .

What is love? 'tis not hereafter;
Present mirth hath present laughter;
   What's to come is still unsure.
In delay there lies no plenty;
Then come kiss me, sweet and twenty;
   Youth's a stuff will not endure.

Unfortunately, most of the original musical settings for Shakespeare's songs have been lost. But just as the plays as a whole have inspired many great composers of music for opera, orchestra, and ballet, so have the songs from the plays been set to music right up to the present.

Varying the Venue

The acting companies performed in two other kinds of spaces: in the great halls of castles and manor houses and in indoor, fully covered theaters in London.

For performances in a great hall, a theater company must have had a portable booth stage. In these buildings the usual entertainment was bearbaiting, a dreadful diversion in which a bear is attacked by dogs. The bear pits were vile places, but their temporary stages could easily accommodate any play except for ones requiring the use of areas overhanging the stage.

Something like the booth stage may also have been used in private theaters like the Blackfriars, which Shakespeare's company, the King's Men, acquired in 1608. One great advantage of the Blackfriars—a former monastery that was entirely roofed over—was that the company could perform there in cold weather and, since there was artificial lighting, at night. Thus, the King's Men could put on plays throughout the year, increasing profits for its owners, among them Shakespeare.

William Shakespeare
(1564–1616)

Every literate person has heard of Shakespeare, the author of more than 36 remarkable plays and more than 150 poems. Over the centuries these literary works have made such a deep impression on the human race that all sorts of fancies, legends, and theories have been invented about their author. There are even those who say that somebody other than Shakespeare wrote the works that bear his name, although these people cannot agree on who, among a dozen candidates, this other author actually was. Such speculation is based on the mis-conception that little is known about Shakespeare's life; in fact, Shakespeare's life is better documented than the life of any other English dramatist of the time except perhaps for Ben Jonson, a writer who seems almost modern in the way he pub-licized himself. Jonson was an honest, blunt, and outspoken man who knew Shakespeare well; for a time the two wrote for the same theatrical company, and Shakespeare even acted in Jonson's plays. Often ungenerous in his judgments of other writers, Jonson published a poem praising Shakespeare, assert-ing that he was superior to all Greek, Roman, and other English dramatists, predicting that he would be "not of an age, but for all time." Jonson's judgment is now commonly accepted, and his prophecy has come true.

The Years in Stratford-on-Avon
Shakespeare was born in Stratford-on-Avon, a historic and prosperous market town in Warwickshire, and was christened in the parish church there on April 26, 1564. His father was John

Shakespeare, a merchant once active in the town government; his mother—born Mary Arden—came from a prominent family in the county. Presumably, for seven years or so, William attended the Stratford grammar school, where he obtained an excellent education in Latin, the Bible, and English composition. (The students were required to translate Latin works into English and then turn them back into Latin.) After leaving school, he may have been apprenticed to a butcher, but because he shows in his plays very detailed knowledge of many different crafts and trades, speculators have proposed a number of different occupations that he could have had. At eighteen, Shakespeare married Anne Hathaway, the twenty-six-year-old daughter of a farmer living near Stratford. They had three children, a daughter named Susanna and twins named Hamnet and Judith. We don't know how the young Shakespeare supported his family, but according to tradition, he taught school for a few years. The two daughters grew up and married; the son died when he was eleven.

Off to London

How did Shakespeare first become interested in the theater? Presumably, by attending performances of plays. We know that traveling acting companies frequently visited Stratford, and we assume that he attended their performances and that he also went to the nearby city of Coventry, where a famous cycle of religious plays was performed every year. In order to be a successful dramatist, however, one had to live in London, where the theater was flourishing in the 1580s. Exactly when Shakespeare left his family and moved to London (there is no evidence that his wife ever accompanied him there) is uncertain; scholars say that he probably arrived in 1587. It is certain that he was busy and successful in the London theater by 1592, when a fellow dramatist named Robert Greene attacked him in print and ridiculed a passage in his early play *Henry VI*. Greene, a down-and-out Cambridge graduate, warned other university men then writing plays to beware of this mere actor who was writing plays—an "upstart crow beautified with our feathers." Greene died of dissipation just as his ill-natured attack was published, but a friend of his named Henry Chettle immediately apologized in print to Shakespeare and commended Shakespeare's acting and writing abilities and his personal honesty.

From 1592 on, there is a fair amount of documentation of Shakespeare's life and works. We know where he lived in London, at least approximately when his plays were produced and printed, and even how he spent some of his money. From 1594 until his retirement in about 1613, he was a member of one company, which also included the great tragic actor Richard Burbage and the popular clown Will Kemp. Although actors and others connected with the theater had very low legal status, in practice they enjoyed the patronage of nobles and even royalty. It is a mistake to think of Shakespeare as an obscure actor who somehow wrote great plays; he was well-known even as a young man. He first became famous as the author of a bestseller, an erotic narrative poem called *Venus and Adonis* (1593). This poem, as well as the more serious poem *The Rape of Lucrece* (1594), was dedicated to a rich and extravagant young nobleman, the earl of Southampton. The dedication of *Lucrece* suggests that Shakespeare and his wealthy patron were on very friendly terms.

Shakespeare's Early Plays: Variety and Prosperity

Among Shakespeare's earliest plays are the following, with the generally but not universally accepted dates of their first performances: *Richard III* (1592–1593), a chronicle or history play about a deformed usurper who became king of England; *The Comedy of Errors* (1592–1593), a rowdy farce about mistaken identity, based on a Latin play; *Titus Andronicus* (1593–1594), a blood-and-thunder tragedy full of rant and atrocities; *The Taming of the Shrew, The Two Gentlemen of Verona,* and *Love's Labor's Lost* (all 1593–1595), three agreeable comedies; and *Romeo and Juliet* (1594–1595), a touching tragedy about ill-fated lovers. The extraordinary thing about these plays is not so much their immense variety—each one differs significantly from the others—but the fact that they are regularly revived and performed on stages around the world today.

Years of Prosperity

By 1596, Shakespeare was beginning to prosper. He had his father apply to the Heralds' College for a coat of arms that the family could display, signifying that they were "gentlefolk," or people of high social standing. On Shakespeare's family crest is a falcon shaking a spear. To support this claim to gentility, Shakespeare bought New Place, a handsome house and grounds in Stratford, a place so commodious and elegant that the queen of England once stayed there after Shakespeare's daughter Susanna inherited it. Shakespeare also, in 1599, joined with a few other members of his company, now called the Lord Chamberlain's Men, to finance a new theater—the famous Globe—on the south side of the River Thames. The "honey-tongued Shakespeare," as he was called in a book about English literature published in 1598, was now earning money as a playwright, an actor, and a shareholder in a theater. By 1600, Shakespeare was regularly associating with members of the aristocracy, and six of his plays had been given command performances at the court of Queen Elizabeth.

During the last years of Elizabeth's reign, Shakespeare completed his cycle of plays about England during the Wars of the Roses: *Richard II* (1595–1596), both parts of *Henry IV* (1596–1597), and *Henry V* (1599). Also in this period he wrote the tragedy *Julius Caesar* (1599)—and the comedies that are most frequently performed today: *A Midsummer Night's*

Dream (1595–1596), *The Merchant of Venice* (1596–1597), *Much Ado About Nothing* (1598–1599), *As You Like It* (1598–1600), and *Twelfth Night* (1600–1601). And finally, at this time he wrote or rewrote *Hamlet* (1600–1601), the tragedy that, of all his tragedies, has provoked the most varied and controversial interpretations from critics, scholars, and actors. Shakespeare indeed prospered under Queen Elizabeth; according to an old tradition, she asked him to write *The Merry Wives of Windsor* (1600–1601) because she wanted to see the merry, fat old knight Sir John Falstaff (of the Henry plays) in love.

Shakespeare prospered even more under Elizabeth's successor, King James of Scotland. Fortunately for Shakespeare's company, as it turned out, James's royal entry into London in 1603 had to be postponed for several months because the plague was raging in the city. While waiting for the epidemic to subside, the royal court stayed in various palaces outside London. Shakespeare's company took advantage of this situation and, since the city theaters were closed, performed several plays for the court and the new king. Shakespeare's plays delighted James, for he loved literature and was starved for pleasure after the grim experience of ruling Scotland for many years. He immediately took the company under his patronage, renamed them the King's Men, permitted them to perform anywhere in the realm, provided them with special clothing for state occasions, increased their salaries, and appointed their chief members, including Shakespeare, to be grooms of the royal chamber. All this patronage brought such prosperity to Shakespeare that he was able to make some very profitable real estate investments in Stratford and London.

Shakespeare's "Tragic Period": Beyond Experience

In the early years of the seventeenth century, while his financial affairs were flourishing and everything was apparently going very well for him, Shakespeare wrote his greatest tragedies:

Hamlet (1600–1601), *Othello* (1601–1602)—which you are about to read—*King Lear* (1605), *Macbeth* (1605–1606), and *Antony and Cleopatra* (1606–1607). Because these famous plays are so preoccupied with evil, violence, and death, some people feel that Shakespeare must have been unhappy and depressed when he wrote them. Moreover, such people find the comedies he wrote at this time more sour than sweet: *All's Well That Ends Well* (1602–1603) and *Measure for Measure* (1604). And so, instead of paying tribute to Shakespeare's powerful imagination, which is everywhere evident, these people invent a "tragic period" in Shakespeare's biography, and they search for personal crises in his private life. When they cannot find these agonies, they invent them. To be sure, in 1607, an actor named Edmund Shakespeare, who may well have been William's younger brother, died in London. But by 1607, Shakespeare's alleged tragic period was almost over.

It is quite wrong to assume a one-to-one correspondence between writers' lives and their works, because writers must be allowed to imagine whatever they can. It is especially wrong in the case of a writer like Shakespeare, who wrote not to express himself but to satisfy the patrons of the theater that he and his partners owned. Shakespeare must have repeatedly given the audience just what it wanted; otherwise, he could not have made so much money from the theater. To insist that he had to experience and personally feel everything that he wrote about is absurd. He wrote about King Lear, who curses his two monstrous daughters for treating him very badly; in contrast, what evidence there is suggests that Shakespeare got along very well with his own daughters. And so we should think of the years 1600–1607 as glorious rather than tragic, because in them Shakespeare's productivity was at its peak. It seems very doubtful that a depressed person would write plays like these. In fact, they would likely make their creator feel exhilarated rather than sad.

The Last Years: Continued Diversity

In about 1610, Shakespeare decided that, having made a considerable sum from his plays and theatrical enterprises, he would retire to his handsome house in Stratford, a place he had never forgotten, though he seems to have kept his life there rather separate from his life in London. His retirement was not complete, for the records show that after he returned to Stratford he still took part in the management of the King's Men and their two theaters: the Globe, a many-sided building opened in 1599 and used for performances in good weather, and the Blackfriars, acquired in 1608 and used for indoor performances. Shakespeare's works in this period show no signs of diminished creativity, except that in some years he wrote one play instead of the customary two, and they continue to illustrate the great diversity of his genius. Among them are the tragedies *Timon of Athens* (1607–1608) and *Coriolanus* (1607–1608) and five plays that have been variously classified as comedies, romances, or tragicomedies: *Pericles* (1607–1608), *Cymbeline* (1609–1610), *The Winter's Tale* (1610–1611), *The Tempest* (1611–1612), and *The Two Noble Kinsmen* (1612). His last English-history play, *Henry VIII* (1613), contained a tribute to Queen Elizabeth—a somewhat tardy tribute, because, unlike most of the other poets of the day, Shakespeare did not praise her in print when she died in 1603. (Some scholars argue, on very little evidence, that he was an admirer of the earl of Essex, a former intimate of Elizabeth whom she had beheaded for rebellion.) During the first performance of *Henry VIII,* in June of 1613, the firing of the cannon at the end of Act I set the Globe on fire (it had a thatched roof), and it burned to the ground. Only one casualty is recorded: A bottle of ale had to be poured on a man whose breeches were burning. Fortunately, the company could perform at the Blackfriars until the Globe was rebuilt in 1614.

Shakespeare's last recorded visit to London was made with his son-in-law Dr. John Hall in November 1614, though he may have gone down to the city afterward because he continued to own property there, including a building very near the Blackfriars Theater. Probably, though, he spent most of the last two years of his life at New Place, with his daughter Susanna Hall (and his granddaughter Elizabeth) living nearby. He died on April 23, 1616, and was buried under the floor of Stratford Church, with this epitaph warning posterity not to dig him up and transfer him to the graveyard outside the church—a common practice in those days to make room for newer corpses:

> Good friend, for Jesus' sake forbear
> To dig the dust enclosèd here!
> Blest be the man that spares these stones,
> And curst be he that moves my bones.

Shakespeare's Genius: Imagination and Soul

What sort of man was Shakespeare? This is a very hard question to answer because he left no letters, diaries, or other private writings containing his personal views; instead, he left us plays, and in a good play the actors speak not for the dramatist but for the characters they are impersonating. We cannot, then, say that Shakespeare approved of evil because he created murderers or advocated religion because he created clergymen; we cannot say that he believed in fatalism because he created fatalists or admired flattery because he created flatterers. All these would be naive, contradictory reactions to the plays. Shakespeare's characters display such a vast range of human behavior and attitudes that they must be products of careful observation and fertile imagination rather than extensions of the playwright. The critic Desmond McCarthy once said that trying to identify Shakespeare the man in his plays is like looking at a very dim portrait under glass: The more you peer at it, the more you see only yourself.

A Complete Man of the Theater

One thing is certain: Shakespeare was a complete man of the theater who created works specifically for his own acting company and his own stage. He had, for instance, to provide good parts in every play for the principal performers in the company, including the comedians acting in tragedies. Since there were no actresses, he had to limit the number of female parts in his plays and create them in such a way that they could readily be taken by boys. For instance, although there are many fathers in the plays, there are very few mothers: While boys could be taught to flirt and play shy, acting maternal would be difficult for them. Several of Shakespeare's young women characters disguise themselves as young men early in Act I—an easy solution to the problem of boys' portraying girls. Shakespeare also had to provide the words for songs because theatergoers expected singing in every play; furthermore, the songs had to be devised so that they would exhibit the talents of particular actors with good voices. Since many of the plays contain many characters, and since there was a limited number of actors in the company, Shakespeare had to arrange for doubling and even tripling of roles: That is, a single actor would have to perform more than one part. Since, of course, an actor could impersonate only one character at a time, Shakespeare had to plan his scenes carefully so that nobody would ever have to be onstage in two different roles at the same time. Shakespeare handled these technical problems masterfully.

Never Out of Print

Although Shakespeare's plays as we know them are primarily performance scripts, from earliest times people have wanted to read them as well as to see them staged. In every generation, people have felt that the plays contain so much wisdom, so much knowledge of human nature, so much remarkable poetry that they need to be pondered in private as well as enjoyed in public. Most readers have agreed with what the poet John Dryden said about Shakespeare's soul: The man who wrote the plays may be elusive, but he was obviously a genius whose lofty imagination is matched by his sympathy for all kinds of human behavior. Reading the plays, then, is a rewarding experience in itself; it is also an excellent preparation for seeing them performed on stage or on film.

Shakespeare's contemporaries were so eager to read his plays that enterprising publishers did everything possible, including stealing them, to make them available. Of course, the company generally tried to keep the plays unpublished because they did not want them performed by rival companies. Even so, eighteen plays were published in small books called quartos before Shakespeare's partners collected and published them after his death. This collection, known as the First Folio because of its large size, was published in 1623. Surviving copies of this edition are regarded as treasures today. But, of course, the general reader need not consult any of the early texts of Shakespeare, because his works never go out of print. The plays that exist in two different versions (one based on a quarto and one on the 1623 folio) have provided scholars with endless matter for speculation about what Shakespeare actually intended the text to be. Indeed, every aspect of Shakespeare has been, and continues to be, thoroughly studied and argued about by specialists in literature and history, theater and film people, experts in many other fields, and amateurs of every stripe. No wonder that he is mistakenly regarded as a great mystery.

The Sources of the Play

The main source for Shakespeare's *Othello* is a collection of stories called *Hecatommithi*, written by Giraldi Cinthio and published in Venice in 1566. It is not known whether Shakespeare read Cinthio in the original Italian or in a French or English translation, but the similarities in plot and subject matter between one of Cinthio's tales and Shakespeare's play are too extensive to be coincidental.

Cinthio's narrative tells of a gallant Moor in the military service of Venice. He falls in love with a beautiful young Venetian woman named Disdemona (the only character identified by name in Cinthio's story). She loves the Moor for his manly virtues and marries him despite opposition from her parents. When the Moor is sent by ship to lead the Venetian troops in Cyprus, his wife travels with him. The Moor's Ensign seeks to win Disdemona and is eaten up with jealous anger when she rejects his advances.

Devious and manipulative, the seemingly upright Ensign (most likely Shakespeare's inspiration for Iago) plots revenge against Disdemona, making use of the Moor and his close friend, the Captain (analogous to Shakespeare's Cassio), who the Ensign believes has had more success with Disdemona than he has. The Ensign steals Disdemona's handkerchief and puts it in the Captain's house, making sure that the Moor sees the Captain leaving Disdemona after he comes to return the handkerchief. Having succeeded in turning the Moor against his wife, the Ensign, with the Moor's help, knocks out Disdemona with a sandbag and lowers a roof beam onto her, hoping to make the death look accidental. Immediately after the murder, the Moor repents his action and grieves for his dead wife, although he still tries to escape punishment. Eventually, the Moor is killed by some of his late wife's relatives, and the Ensign is brought to justice for another crime.

Although the similarities to Shakespeare's *Othello* are clear (the interracial marriage, the wrongly accused wife, the husband misled by a villainous subordinate, and the seemingly incriminating handkerchief), the differences are equally apparent. Cinthio's story is a shallow, melodramatic tale of sexual jealousy and sordid revenge. While distinguished, his Moor is hardly noble, and the reader feels little or no sympathy or fear at his fall, only pity for his innocent victim. Shakespeare, on the other hand, gives Othello dignity and stature not only by the great lines he speaks but also by the deep and moving love he sustains for the woman he murders. In the end Shakespeare's tragic hero, unlike Cinthio's, acknowledges his terrible crime and passes judgment upon himself by taking his own life.

The seeds of Iago's personality can certainly be found in the Ensign in Cinthio's story. But without a character like Roderigo, Iago's confederate and dupe, and the device of the soliloquy, there is far less penetration into the villain's motives than in Shakespeare. Cinthio's Ensign is motivated mainly by sexual jealousy. Disdemona, not the Moor or his Captain, is his principal target. The Ensign's motives and means are far cruder than those of Shakespeare's Iago, and so his deeds inspire an emotional response that is simpler than the awe and perplexity that Iago's cruel calculations produce in Shakespeare's audience. As the critic John Russell Brown writes, "From [Cinthio's] sordid tale, [Shakespeare's] tragedy arose, creating potent images of heaven and hell, fate and freedom, love and hate, isolation and union."

Another source for *Othello* may be the fourth story in Geoffrey Fenton's collection *Certain Tragical Discourses* (1567). This includes a tale of jealousy set during a war with the Ottoman Turks. A man, suspecting his wife of infidelity, kisses her and then kills her in their bedroom. Like Othello, the man then kills himself and falls upon the body of his dead wife.

There is also evidence that Shakespeare took some of the details of Othello's travels (the Anthropophagi, chrysolite, the Pontic Sea) from Philemon Holland's English translation (1601) of *Natural History* by Pliny the Elder, an ancient Roman who wrote on scientific topics. Shakespeare may also have taken political and historical background from Richard Knolles's *General History of the Turks* (1603) and from an English translation (1599) of Cardinal Contarini's *Commonwealth and Government of Venice.*

The Tragedy of Othello

The Moor of Venice

by
William Shakespeare

Dramatis Personae

OTHELLO, a noble Moor, and a general in the service of the Venetian state.

BRABANTIO, a senator, and father to Desdemona.

CASSIO, honorable lieutenant to Othello.

IAGO, villainous ancient to Othello.

RODERIGO, a gulled Venetian gentleman.

DUKE OF VENICE.

DESDEMONA, daughter to Brabantio, and wife to Othello.

EMILIA, wife to Iago.

BIANCA, mistress to Cassio.

MONTANO, Othello's predecessor as governor of Cyprus.

GRATIANO, a noble Venetian, and brother to Brabantio.

LODOVICO, a noble Venetian, and kinsman to Brabantio.

SENATORS of Venice.

CLOWN, servant to Othello.

SAILOR, MESSENGER, HERALD, OFFICERS, GENTLEMEN, MUSICIANS, and ATTENDANTS.

Act I

Scene 1. *Venice. A street.*

Enter RODERIGO *and* IAGO.

Roderigo.
    Tush! Never tell me; I take it much unkindly
    That thou, Iago, who hast had my purse
    As if the strings were thine, shouldst know of this.
Iago.
    'Sblood,° but you will not hear me! If ever I did dream
    Of such a matter, abhor me.
Roderigo.   Thou told'st me   5
    Thou didst hold him in thy hate.
Iago.   Despise me,
    If I do not. Three great ones of the city,
    In personal suit to make me his lieutenant,
    Off-capped° to him; and, by the faith of man,
    I know my price; I am worth no worse a place.   10
    But he, as loving his own pride and purposes,
    Evades them with a bombast circumstance,°
    Horribly stuffed with epithets of war;
    And, in conclusion,
    Nonsuits° my mediators. For, "Certes," says he,   15
    "I have already chose my officer." And what was he?
    Forsooth, a great arithmetician,°
    One Michael Cassio, a Florentine,
    A fellow almost damned in a fair wife,°

I.1.4. 'Sblood: God's blood (a swearword).
  9. Off-capp'd: doffed (took off) their caps (to show respect).
  12. bombast circumstance: pompous, evasive speech.
  15. Nonsuits: rejects.
  17. arithmetician: one skilled in theory rather than practice.
  19. A fellow . . . wife: (The meaning of the line is not fully clear, for Cassio is not married in the play. In general, however, Iago is expressing contempt for Cassio as a lady's man.)

That never set a squadron in the field,   20
Nor the division of a battle knows
More than a spinster; unless the bookish theoric,
Wherein the tonguèd° consuls can propose
As masterly as he. Mere prattle, without practice
Is all his soldiership. But he, sir, had th' election: 25
And I, of whom his eyes had seen the proof
At Rhodes, at Cyprus and on other grounds
Christian and heathen, must be belee'd° and calmed
By debitor and creditor. This counter-caster,°
He, in good time, must his lieutenant be,   30
And I—God bless the mark!—his Moorship's ancient.°

Roderigo.

By heaven, I rather would have been his hangman.

Iago.

Why, there's no remedy. 'Tis the curse of service:
Preferment goes by letter and affection,
And not by old gradation,° where each second   35
Stood heir to the first. Now, sir, be judge yourself
Whether I in any just term am affined°
To love the Moor.

Roderigo.   I would not follow him then.

Iago.

O, sir, content you;
I follow him to serve my turn upon him.   40
We cannot all be masters, nor all masters
Cannot be truly followed. You shall mark
Many a duteous and knee-crooking knave
That, doting on his own obsequious bondage,
Wears out his time, much like his master's ass,   45

---

23. **tonguèd:** well-spoken; eloquent.
28. **belee'd:** sailing ship sheltered from wind and thus unable to move.
29. **counter-caster:** bookkeeper who casts (calculates) figures on a
     counter (abacus).
31. **ancient:** flag carrier; officer ranking lower than a lieutenant.
35. **old gradation:** seniority.
37. **affined:** required.

For naught but provender;° and when he's old,
   cashiered.
Whip me such honest knaves! Others there are
Who, trimmed in forms and visages of duty,
Keep yet their hearts attending on themselves,
And, throwing but shows of service on their lords,   50
Do well thrive by them; and when they have lined
   their coats,
Do themselves homage. These fellows have some
   soul,
And such a one do I profess myself. For, sir,
It is as sure as you are Roderigo,
Were I the Moor, I would not be Iago.   55
In following him, I follow but myself.
Heaven is my judge, not I for love and duty,
But seeming so, for my peculiar° end.
For when my outward action doth demonstrate
The native° act and figure of my heart   60
In complement extern,° 'tis not long after
But I will wear my heart upon my sleeve
For daws° to peck at. I am not what I am.

Roderigo.
What a full fortune does the thick-lips owe°
If he can carry't thus!

Iago.   Call up her father: 65
Rouse him. Make after him, poison his delight,
Proclaim him in the streets, incense her kinsmen,
And though he in a fertile climate dwell,
Plague him with flies: though that his joy be joy,
Yet throw such changes of vexation on't   70
As it may lose some color.

---

46. **provender:** food.
58. **peculiar:** personal.
60. **native:** inborn; natural.
61. **complement extern:** external or outward appearance.
63. **daws:** jackdaws; small crows.
64. **owe:** own; possess.

Roderigo.

Here is her father's house. I'll call aloud.

Iago.

Do, with like timorous° accent and dire yell

As when, by night and negligence, the fire

Is spied in populous cities.   75

Roderigo.

What, ho, Brabantio! Signior Brabantio, ho!

Iago.

Awake! what, ho, Brabantio! Thieves! Thieves!

Look to your house, your daughter, and your bags!

Thieves! Thieves!

BRABANTIO *appears above,° at a window.*

Brabantio.

What is the reason of this terrible summons?   80

What is the matter there?

Roderigo.

Signior, is all your family within?

Iago.

Are your doors locked?

Brabantio.   Why, wherefore ask you this?

Iago.

Zounds,° sir, y'are robbed! For shame, put on your
    gown!

Your heart is burst, you have lost half your soul.   85

Even now, now, very now, an old black ram

Is topping your white ewe. Arise, arise!

Awake the snorting citizens with the bell,

Or else the devil will make a grandsire of you.

Arise, I say!

Brabantio.   What, have you lost your wits?   90

---

73. **timorous:** frightening.

s.d. **above:** that is, on the gallery above the Globe stage, often used in
    plays by Shakespeare.

84. **Zounds:** God's wounds (a swearword).

Roderigo.
Most reverend signior, do you know my voice?
Brabantio.
Not I. What are you?
Roderigo.
My name is Roderigo.
Brabantio.   The worser welcome.
I have charged thee not to haunt about my doors.
In honest plainness thou hast heard me say   95
My daughter is not for thee; and now, in madness,
Being full of supper and distemp'ring draughts,°
Upon malicious bravery dost thou come
To start° my quiet.
Roderigo.
Sir, sir, sir—
Brabantio.   But thou must needs be sure   100
My spirit and my place° have in their power
To make this bitter to thee.
Roderigo.   Patience, good sir.
Brabantio.
What tell'st thou me of robbing? This is Venice;
My house is not a grange.°
Roderigo.   Most grave Brabantio,
In simple and pure soul I come to you.   105
Iago. Zounds, sir, you are one of those that will not
serve God if the devil bid you. Because we come to
do you service and you think we are ruffians, you'll
have your daughter covered with a Barbary horse;
you'll have your nephews° neigh to you; you'll have   110
coursers° for cousins and gennets for germans.°

---

97. **distemp'ring draughts:** agitating alcoholic drinks.
99. **start:** interrupt.
101. **place:** position as senator.
104. **grange:** isolated house.
110. **nephews:** here, grandsons.
111. **coursers:** swift horses; chargers. **gennets for germans:** Spanish horses
   for relatives.

Brabantio.

What profane wretch art thou?

Iago. I am one, sir, that comes to tell you your daughter and
the Moor are now making the beast with two backs.

Brabantio.

Thou art a villain.

Iago.   You are—a senator.   115

Brabantio.

This thou shalt answer. I know thee, Roderigo.

Roderigo.

Sir, I will answer anything. But I beseech you,
If't be your pleasure and most wise consent,
As partly I find it is, that your fair daughter,
At this odd-even° and dull watch o' th' night,   120
Transported, with no worse nor better guard
But with a knave of common hire, a gondolier,
To the gross clasps of a lascivious Moor—
If this be known to you, and your allowance,
We then have done you bold and saucy wrongs.   125
But if you know not this, my manners tell me
We have your wrong rebuke. Do not believe
That from the sense of all civility,
I thus would play and trifle with your reverence.
Your daughter, if you have not given her leave,   130
I say again, hath made a gross revolt,
Tying her duty, beauty, wit, and fortunes
In an extravagant° and wheeling stranger
Of here and everywhere. Straight satisfy yourself.
If she be in her chamber or your house,   135
Let loose on me the justice of the state
For thus deluding you.

Brabantio.   Strike on the tinder, ho!

Give me a taper! Call up all my people!
This accident° is not unlike my dream.

---

120. **odd-even:** time between night and morning.
133. **extravagant:** wandering; roaming. (Othello is not a Venetian.)
139. **accident:** occurrence; incident.

Belief of it oppresses me already.   140
Light, I say! Light!   [*Exit above.*]

Iago.   Farewell, for I must leave you.
   It seems not meet, nor wholesome to my place,
   To be produced—as, if I stay, I shall—
   Against the Moor. For I do know the state,
   However this may gall him with some check,°   145
   Cannot with safety cast° him; for he's embarked
   With such loud reason to the Cyprus wars,
   Which even now stand in act,° that, for their souls,
   Another of his fathom° they have none
   To lead their business; in which regard,   150
   Though I do hate him as I do hell-pains,
   Yet, for necessity of present life,
   I must show out a flag and sign of love,
   Which is indeed but sign. That you shall surely find
      him,
   Lead to the Sagittary° the raisèd search;   155
   And there will I be with him. So farewell.   [*Exit.*]

Enter BRABANTIO *in his nightgown and* SERVANTS *with torches.*

Brabantio.
   It is too true an evil. Gone she is;
   And what's to come of my despisèd time
   Is naught but bitterness. Now, Roderigo,
   Where didst thou see her?—O unhappy girl!—   160
   With the Moor, say'st thou?—Who would be a
      father!—
   How didst thou know 'twas she?—O, she deceives me
   Past thought!—What said she to you? Get moe tapers!
   Raise all my kindred!—Are they married, think you?

---

145. **check:** restraint.
146. **cast:** discharge.
148. **stand in act:** are taking place.
149. **fathom:** skill; talent.
155. **Sagittary:** (probably an inn).

Roderigo.

    Truly I think they are.   165

Brabantio.

    O heaven! How got she out? O treason of the blood!

    Fathers, from hence trust not your daughters' minds

    By what you see them act. Is there not charms

    By which the property° of youth and maidhood

    May be abused? Have you not read, Roderigo,   170

    Of some such thing?

Roderigo.   Yes, sir, I have indeed.

Brabantio.

    Call up my brother.—O, would you had had her!—

    Some one way, some another.—Do you know

    Where we may apprehend her and the Moor?

Roderigo.

    I think I can discover him, if you please   175

    To get good guard and go along with me.

Brabantio.

    Pray you lead on. At every house I'll call;

    I may command at most.—Get weapons, ho!

    And raise some special officers of night.—

    On, good Roderigo; I'll deserve your pains.°   180

                                Exeunt.

Scene 2. *Another street.*

Enter OTHELLO, IAGO, *and* ATTENDANTS *with torches.*

Iago.

    Though in the trade of war I have slain men,

    Yet do I hold it very stuff° o' th' conscience

---

169. **property:** real nature.
180. **deserve your pains:** be worthy of, and reward, your efforts.
I.2.2. **very stuff:** essential material.

To do no contrived murder. I lack iniquity
Sometimes to do me service. Nine or ten times
I had thought t' have yerked° him° here, under the ribs.   5
Othello.
'Tis better as it is.
Iago.   Nay, but he prated,
And spoke such scurvy° and provoking terms
Against your honor, that, with the little godliness I
   have,
I did full hard forbear him. But, I pray you, sir,
Are you fast° married? Be assured of this,   10
That the magnifico° is much beloved,
And hath in his effect° a voice potential
As double as the duke's. He will divorce you,
Or put upon you what restraint and grievance°
The law, with all his might to enforce it on,   15
Will give him cable.°
Othello.   Let him do his spite.
My services which I have done the Signiory°
Shall out-tongue his complaints. 'Tis yet to know—
Which, when I know that boasting is an honor,
I shall promulgate—I fetch my life and being   20
From men of royal siege;° and my demerits°
May speak unbonneted° to as proud a fortune
As this that I have reached. For know, Iago,
But that I love the gentle Desdemona,
I would not my unhousèd free condition   25

---

5. **yerked:** stabbed. **him:** Roderigo.
7. **scurvy:** insulting.
10. **fast:** firmly.
11. **magnifico:** nobleman, that is, Brabantio.
12. **in his effect:** at his command.
14. **grievance:** punishment.
16. **cable:** scope; range.
17. **Signiory:** Venetian government.
21. **siege:** rank. **demerits:** worthiness.
22. **unbonneted:** without removing the hat; that is, on equal terms.

Put into circumscription and confine
For the sea's worth.° But, look! what lights come
    yond?

Enter CASSIO *and certain* OFFICERS *with torches.*

Iago.
Those are the raisèd father and his friends.
You were best go in.
Othello.   Not I. I must be found.
My parts, my title, and my perfect soul°   30
Shall manifest me rightly. Is it they?
Iago.
By Janus,° I think no.
Othello.
The servants of the duke? And my lieutenant?
The goodness of the night upon you, friends!
What is the news?
Cassio.   The duke does greet you, general;   35
And he requires your haste-post-haste appearance
Even on the instant.
Othello.   What is the matter, think you?
Cassio.
Something from Cyprus, as I may divine.
It is a business of some heat. The galleys
Have sent a dozen sequent° messengers   40
This very night at one another's heels,
And many of the consuls, raised and met,
Are at the duke's already. You have been hotly
    called for.
When, being not at your lodging to be found,
The Senate hath sent about three several° quests   45
To search you out.

---

27. **sea's worth:** treasures lying at the bottom of the sea.
30. **perfect soul:** clear conscience.
32. **Janus:** Roman god of beginnings, typically shown as having two faces.
40. **sequent:** successive.
45. **several:** separate.

Othello.   'Tis well I am found by you.
I will but spend a word here in the house,
And go with you.   [*Exit.*]
Cassio.   Ancient, what makes he here?
Iago.
Faith, he tonight hath boarded a land carack.°
If it prove lawful prize, he's made forever.   50
Cassio.
I do not understand.
Iago.   He's married.
Cassio.   To who?

Enter OTHELLO.

Iago.
Marry,° to—Come, captain, will you go?
Othello.   Have with you.
Cassio.
Here comes another troop to seek for you.

Enter BRABANTIO, RODERIGO, *and* OFFICERS *with torches
and weapons.*

Iago.
It is Brabantio. General, be advised.
He comes to bad intent.
Othello.   Holla! stand there!   55
Roderigo.
Signior, it is the Moor.
Brabantio.   Down with him, thief!

They draw swords.

Iago.
You, Roderigo! Come, sir, I am for you.
Othello.
Keep up your bright swords, for the dew will rust
    them.

---

49. carack: large treasure ship.
52. Marry: a mild oath; originally "By the Virgin Mary."

Good signior, you shall more command with years
Than with your weapons.   60
Brabantio.
O thou foul thief, where hast thou stowed my
    daughter?
Damned as thou art, thou hast enchanted her!
For I'll refer me to all things of sense,°
If she in chains of magic were not bound,
Whether a maid so tender, fair, and happy,   65
So opposite to marriage that she shunned
The wealthy curlèd darlings of our nation,
Would ever have, t' incur a general mock,°
Run from her guardage to the sooty bosom
Of such a thing as thou—to fear, not to delight.   70
Judge me the world if 'tis not gross in sense°
That thou hast practiced on her with foul charms,
Abused her delicate youth with drugs or minerals
That weaken motion.° I'll have't disputed on;
'Tis probable, and palpable to thinking.   75
I therefore apprehend and do attach° thee
For an abuser of the world, a practicer
Of arts inhibited and out of warrant.°
Lay hold upon him. If he do resist,
Subdue him at his peril.
Othello.   Hold your hands,   80
Both you of my inclining° and the rest.
Were it my cue to fight, I should have known it
Without a prompter. Whither will you that I go
To answer this your charge?

---

63. **things of sense:** reasonable creatures or assumptions.
68. **general mock:** public ridicule.
71. **gross in sense:** obvious.
74. **weaken motion:** dull the senses.
76. **attach:** arrest.
78. **arts . . . warrant:** illegal magical practices.
81. **of my inclining:** on my side.

Brabantio.   To prison, till fit time
    Of law and course of direct session°   85
    Call thee to answer.
Othello.   What if I do obey?
    How may the duke be therewith satisfied,
    Whose messengers are here about my side
    Upon some present° business of the state
    To bring me to him?
Officer.   'Tis true, most worthy signior.   90
    The duke's in council and your noble self,
    I am sure is sent for.
Brabantio.   How? The duke in council?
    In this time of the night? Bring him away.
    Mine's not an idle cause. The duke himself,
    Or any of my brothers of the state,°   95
    Cannot but feel this wrong as 'twere their own;
    For if such actions may have passage free,
    Bond-slaves and pagans shall our statesmen be.

                                 Exeunt.

Scene 3. *A council chamber.*

The DUKE *and* SENATORS *sit at a table;* OFFICERS *attend.*

Duke of Venice.
    There is no composition° in these news
    That gives them credit.°
First Senator.   Indeed, they are disproportioned.
    My letters say a hundred and seven galleys.

---

  85. **course of direct session:** court session.
  89. **present:** immediate.
  95. **brothers of the state:** fellow senators.
I.3.1. **composition:** agreement.
   2. **credit:** believability.

Duke of Venice.

And mine, a hundred and forty.

Second Senator.   And mine, two hundred.

But though they jump° not on a just° accompt—   5

As in these cases where the aim° reports

'Tis oft with difference—yet do they all confirm

A Turkish fleet, and bearing up to Cyprus.

Duke of Venice.

Nay, it is possible enough to judgment.°

I do not so secure me in the error,   10

But the main article I do approve

In fearful sense.°

Sailor. [*Within.*]   What, ho! What, ho! What, ho!

Enter SAILOR.

Officer.

A messenger from the galleys.

Duke of Venice.   Now? What's the business?

Sailor.

The Turkish preparation makes for Rhodes.

So was I bid report here to the state   15

By Signior Angelo.

Duke of Venice.

How say you by this change?

First Senator.   This cannot be,

By no assay° of reason. 'Tis a pageant°

To keep us in false gaze.° When we consider

Th' importancy of Cyprus to the Turk,   20

And let ourselves again but understand

That as it more concerns the Turk than Rhodes,

---

   5. **jump:** agree. **just:** exact.
   6. **aim:** estimate.
   9. **to judgment:** when carefully considered.
11–12. **the main . . . sense:** the basic information is cause for alarm.
  18. **assay:** test. **pageant:** mere show; pretense.
  19. **in false gaze:** looking in the wrong direction.

So may he with more facile question bear it,°
For that it stands not in such warlike brace,°
But altogether lacks th' abilities   25
That Rhodes is dressed in. If we make thought of
     this,
We must not think the Turk is so unskillful
To leave that latest which concerns him first,
Neglecting an attempt of ease and gain
To wake and wage a danger profitless.   30

Duke of Venice.
Nay, in all confidence he's not for Rhodes.

Officer.
Here is more news.

Enter a MESSENGER.

Messenger.
The Ottomites, reverend and gracious,
Steering with due course toward the isle of Rhodes,
Have there injointed them with an after° fleet.   35

First Senator.
Ay, so I thought. How many, as you guess?

Messenger.
Of thirty sail; and now they do restem
Their backward course, bearing with frank
     appearance
Their purposes toward Cyprus. Signior Montano,
Your trusty and most valiant servitor,   40
With his free duty recommends° you thus,
And prays you to believe him.

Duke of Venice.
'Tis certain, then, for Cyprus.
Marcus Luccicos, is not he in town?

---

23. **may . . . it:** (the Turk) can more easily capture it (Cyprus).
24. **warlike brace:** military preparedness.
35. **after:** following; second.
41. **recommends:** informs.

First Senator.

He's now in Florence.

Duke of Venice.   Write from us to him   45

Post-post-haste dispatch.

First Senator.

Here comes Brabantio and the valiant Moor.

Enter BRABANTIO, OTHELLO, CASSIO, IAGO, RODERIGO, *and*
OFFICERS.

Duke of Venice.

Valiant Othello, we must straight° employ you

Against the general° enemy Ottoman.

To BRABANTIO.

I did not see you. Welcome, gentle signior.   50

We lacked your counsel and your help tonight.

Brabantio.

So did I yours. Good your grace, pardon me.

Neither my place, nor aught I heard of business,

Hath raised me from my bed; nor doth the general
care

Take hold on me; for my particular grief   55

Is of so floodgate and o'erbearing nature

That it engluts and swallows other sorrows,

And it is still itself.

Duke of Venice.   Why, what's the matter?

Brabantio.

My daughter! O, my daughter!

Senators.   Dead?

Brabantio.   Ay, to me.

She is abused, stol'n from me, and corrupted   60

By spells and medicines bought of mountebanks;°

For nature so prepost'rously to err,

---

48. **straight:** immediately.
49. **general:** universal (because seen as opposed to Christianity).
61. **mountebanks:** charlatans.

Being not deficient, blind, or lame of sense,
Sans° witchcraft could not.

Duke of Venice.
Whoe'er he be that in this foul proceeding   65
Hath thus beguiled your daughter of herself,
And you of her, the bloody book of law
You shall yourself read in the bitter letter
After your own sense; yea, though our proper° son
Stood in your action.°

Brabantio.   Humbly I thank your grace.   70
Here is the man—this Moor, whom now, it seems,
Your special mandate for the state affairs
Hath hither brought.

All.   We are very sorry for't.

Duke of Venice. [*To* OTHELLO.]
What in your own part can you say to this?

Brabantio.
Nothing, but this is so.   75

Othello.
Most potent, grave, and reverend signiors,
My very noble and approved° good masters,
That I have ta'en away this old man's daughter,
It is most true; true, I have married her.
The very head and front° of my offending   80
Hath this extent, no more. Rude am I in my speech,
And little blessed with the soft phrase of peace,
For since these arms of mine had seven years' pith°
Till now some nine moons wasted, they have used
Their dearest° action in the tented field;   85
And little of this great world can I speak

---

64. **Sans:** without.
69. **our proper:** my own.
70. **Stood in your action:** faced your accusation.
77. **approved:** esteemed.
80. **head and front:** height and breadth (that is, the entire extent).
83. **pith:** strength.
85. **dearest:** most important.

More than pertains to feats of broils and battle;
And therefore little shall I grace my cause
In speaking for myself. Yet, by your gracious patience,
I will a round° unvarnished tale deliver   90
Of my whole course of love—what drugs, what
    charms,
What conjuration, and what mighty magic,
For such proceeding I am charged withal,
I won his daughter—
Brabantio.   A maiden never bold;
Of spirit so still and quiet that her motion   95
Blushed at herself;° and she, in spite of nature,
Of years, of country, credit, everything,
To fall in love with what she feared to look on!
It is a judgment maimed and most imperfect
That will confess perfection so could err   100
Against all rules of nature, and must be driven
To find out practices of cunning hell
Why this should be. I therefore vouch again
That with some mixtures pow'rful o'er the blood,°
Or with some dram, conjured to this effect,   105
He wrought upon her.
Duke of Venice.   To vouch this is no proof,
Without more wider and more overt test
Than these thin habits° and poor likelihoods
Of modern seeming° do prefer against him.
First Senator.
But, Othello, speak.   110
Did you by indirect and forcèd courses
Subdue and poison this young maid's affections?
Or came it by request, and such fair question°
As soul to soul affordeth?

---

90. **round:** plain; blunt.
95–96. **her . . . herself:** she was embarrassed by her feelings.
104. **blood:** passions.
108. **habits:** clothing; hence, outward appearances.
109. **modern seeming:** commonplace assumptions.
113. **question:** conversation.

Othello.   I do beseech you,
   Send for the lady to the Sagittary,   115
   And let her speak of me before her father:
   If you do find me foul in her report,
   The trust, the office, I do hold of you,
   Not only take away, but let your sentence
   Even fall upon my life.
Duke of Venice.   Fetch Desdemona hither.   120
Othello.
   Ancient, conduct them; you best know the place.

                    Exeunt IAGO *and* ATTENDANTS.

   And till she come, as truly as to heaven
   I do confess the vices of my blood,
   So justly to your grave ears I'll present
   How I did thrive in this fair lady's love,   125
   And she in mine.
Duke of Venice.   Say it, Othello.
Othello.
   Her father loved me; oft invited me;
   Still° questioned me the story of my life
   From year to year, the battles, sieges, fortunes
   That I have passed.   130
   I ran it through, even from my boyish days
   To th' very moment that he bade me tell it.
   Wherein I spake of most disastrous chances,
   Of moving accidents by flood and field,
   Of hairbreadth scapes i' th' imminent deadly breach,°   135
   Of being taken by the insolent foe
   And sold to slavery; of my redemption thence
   And portance° in my travels' history:
   Wherein of antres° vast and deserts idle,°

---

128. Still: continually.
135. imminent deadly breach: life-threatening gaps in a fortification.
138. portance: conduct.
139. antres: caves. **idle:** empty; desolate.

Rough quarries, rocks, and hills whose heads touch
    heaven,   140
It was my hint to speak. Such was the process.
And of the Cannibals that each other eat,
The Anthropophagi,° and men whose heads
Grew beneath their shoulders. These things to hear
Would Desdemona seriously incline;   145
But still the house affairs would draw her thence;
Which ever as she could with haste dispatch,
She'd come again, and with a greedy ear
Devour up my discourse. Which I observing,
Took once a pliant° hour, and found good means   150
To draw from her a prayer of earnest heart
That I would all my pilgrimage dilate,°
Whereof by parcels she had something heard,
But not intentively.° I did consent,
And often did beguile her of° her tears   155
When I did speak of some distressful stroke
That my youth suffered. My story being done,
She gave me for my pains a world of kisses.
She swore, in faith, 'twas strange, 'twas passing°
    strange,
'Twas pitiful, 'twas wondrous pitiful.   160
She wished she had not heard it, yet she wished
That heaven had made her such a man. She
    thanked me,
And bade me, if I had a friend that loved her,
I should but teach him how to tell my story,
And that would woo her. Upon this hint I spake.   165
She loved me for the dangers I had passed,
And I loved her that she did pity them.

---

143. **Anthropophagi:** man-eaters; cannibals.
150. **pliant:** suitable.
152. **dilate:** tell in full.
154. **intentively:** with continuous attention.
155. **beguile her of:** coax from her.
159. **passing:** exceedingly.

This only is the witchcraft I have used.
Here comes the lady. Let her witness it.

Enter DESDEMONA, IAGO, *and* ATTENDANTS.

Duke of Venice.
    I think this tale would win my daughter too.   170
    Good Brabantio, take up this mangled matter at the
        best.°
    Men do their broken weapons rather use
    Than their bare hands.
Brabantio.   I pray you hear her speak.
    If she confess that she was half the wooer,
    Destruction on my head if my bad blame   175
    Light on the man! Come hither, gentle mistress.
    Do you perceive in all this noble company
    Where most you owe obedience?
Desdemona.   My noble father,
    I do perceive here a divided duty:
    To you I am bound for life and education;°   180
    My life and education both do learn me
    How to respect you. You are lord of all my duty;
    I am hitherto your daughter. But here's my husband;
    And so much duty as my mother showed
    To you, preferring you before her father,   185
    So much I challenge° that I may profess
    Due to the Moor my lord.
Brabantio.   God be with you! I have done.
    Please it your grace, on to the state affairs.
    I had rather to adopt a child than get° it.
    Come hither, Moor: 190
    I here do give thee that with all my heart
    Which, but thou hast already, with all my heart

---

171. **take . . . best:** make the best of a bad bargain.
180. **education:** upbringing.
186. **challenge:** claim.
189. **get:** beget.

I would keep from thee. For your sake,° jewel,
I am glad at soul I have no other child,
For thy escape would teach me tyranny,   195
To hang clogs on them. I have done, my lord.

Duke of Venice.

Let me speak like yourself and lay a sentence°
Which, as a grise° or step, may help these lovers
Into your favor.
When remedies are past, the griefs are ended   200
By seeing the worst, which late on hopes depended.°
To mourn a mischief° that is past and gone
Is the next° way to draw new mischief on.
What cannot be preserved when fortune takes,
Patience her injury a mock'ry makes.   205
The robbed that smiles steals something from the
    thief;
He robs himself that spends a bootless° grief.

Brabantio.

So let the Turk of Cyprus us beguile;
We lose it not, so long as we can smile.
He bears the sentence well that nothing bears   210
But the free comfort which from thence he hears;
But he bears both the sentence and the sorrow
That to pay grief must of poor patience borrow.
These sentences, to sugar or to gall,
Being strong on both sides, are equivocal.   215
But words are words; I never yet did hear
That the bruisèd heart was piercèd through the ear.°
I humbly beseech you, proceed to th' affairs of state.

---

193. **For your sake:** because of you.
197. **lay a sentence:** provide a maxim.
198. **grise:** step.
201. **late on hopes depended:** were supported until recently by hopeful
    expectations.
202. **mischief:** misfortune.
203. **next:** nearest; likeliest.
207. **bootless:** unavailing.
217. **bruisèd . . . ear:** broken heart was cured by words.

Duke of Venice. The Turk with a most mighty preparation
    makes for Cyprus. Othello, the fortitude° of the place   220
    is best known to you; and though we have there a
    substitute° of most allowed sufficiency, yet opinion, a
    more sovereign mistress of effects, throws a more
    safer voice on you.° You must therefore be content to
    slubber° the gloss of your new fortunes with this more   225
    stubborn and boisterous° expedition.

Othello.
    The tyrant Custom, most grave senators,
    Hath made the flinty and steel couch of war
    My thrice-driven° bed of down. I do agnize°
    A natural and prompt alacrity   230
    I find in hardness, and do undertake
    These present wars against the Ottomites.
    Most humbly, therefore, bending to your state,°
    I crave fit disposition for my wife,
    Due reference of place and exhibition,°   235
    With such accommodation and besort
    As levels with her breeding.

Duke of Venice.   Why, at her father's.

Brabantio.
    I'll not have it so.

Othello.   Nor I.

Desdemona.   Nor would I there reside,
    To put my father in impatient thoughts
    By being in his eye. Most gracious duke,   240
    To my unfolding° lend your prosperous° ear,

---

220. **fortitude:** defensive strength.
222. **substitute:** deputy.
223–224. **throws . . . you:** judges you the more reliable.
225. **slubber:** soil; sully.
226. **stubborn and boisterous:** harsh and violent.
229. **thrice-driven:** softest (like fine sand that has been driven, or sifted, three times). **agnize:** acknowledge.
233. **state:** authority.
235. **place and exhibition:** residence and financial support.
241. **unfolding:** explanation. **prosperous:** favoring.

And let me find a charter° in your voice,
T' assist my simpleness.
Duke of Venice.   What would you, Desdemona?
Desdemona.
    That I love the Moor to live with him,
    My downright violence° and storm of fortunes   245
    May trumpet to the world. My heart's subdued
    Even to the very quality° of my lord.
    I saw Othello's visage in his mind,
    And to his honors and his valiant parts
    Did I my soul and fortunes consecrate.   250
    So that, dear lords, if I be left behind,
    A moth of peace, and he go to the war,
    The rites for which I love him are bereft me,
    And I a heavy interim shall support
    By his dear absence. Let me go with him.   255
Othello.
    Let her have your voice.°
    Vouch with me, heaven, I therefore beg it not
    To please the palate of my appetite,
    Nor to comply with heat—the young affects°
    In me defunct—and proper° satisfaction;   260
    But to be free and bounteous to her mind;
    And heaven defend° your good souls that you think
    I will your serious and great business scant
    When she is with me. No, when light-winged toys
    Of feathered Cupid seel° with wanton dullness   265

---

242. **charter:** permission.
245. **downright violence:** absolute violation of the norm.
247. **quality:** nature.
256. **voice:** consent.
259. **affects:** passions.
260. **proper:** personal.
262. **defend:** forbid.
265. **seel:** blind (from falconry, in which the eyes of a young hawk are
        seeled, or sewn closed, during training).

My speculative and officed instruments,°
That my disports corrupt and taint my business,
Let housewives make a skillet of my helm,
And all indign° and base adversities
Make head° against my estimation!°   270

Duke of Venice.
Be it as you shall privately determine,
Either for her stay or going. Th' affair cries haste,
And speed must answer it.

First Senator.   You must away tonight.

Desdemona.
Tonight, my lord?

Duke of Venice.   This night.

Othello.   With all my heart.

Duke of Venice.
At nine i' th' morning here we'll meet again.   275
Othello, leave some officer behind,
And he shall our commission bring to you,
With such things else of quality and respect
As doth import you.

Othello.   So please your grace, my ancient;
A man he is of honesty and trust.   280
To his conveyance I assign my wife,
With what else needful your good grace shall think
To be sent after me.

Duke of Venice.   Let it be so.
Good night to every one. [*To* BRABANTIO.] And,
    noble signior,
If virtue no delighted° beauty lack,   285
Your son-in-law is far more fair than black.

First Senator.
Adieu, brave Moor. Use Desdemona well.

---

266. speculative . . . instruments: perceptive senses (sight and reasoning) used in performance of duty.
269. indign: unworthy.
270. Make head: mount an attack. **estimation:** reputation.
285. delighted: delightful.

Brabantio.

Look to her, Moor, if thou hast eyes to see:
She has deceived her father, and may thee.

Exeunt DUKE OF VENICE, SENATORS, OFFICERS, *etc.*

Othello.

My life upon her faith! Honest Iago,   290
My Desdemona must I leave to thee.
I prithee, let thy wife attend on her,
And bring her after in the best advantage.°
Come, Desdemona. I have but an hour
Of love, of worldly matters and direction,   295
To spend with thee. We must obey the time.

Exeunt OTHELLO *and* DESDEMONA.

Roderigo. Iago?
Iago. What say'st thou, noble heart?
Roderigo. What will I do, think'st thou?
Iago. Why, go to bed and sleep.   300
Roderigo. I will incontinently° drown myself.
Iago. If thou dost, I shall never love thee after. Why,
thou silly gentleman?
Roderigo. It is silliness to live when to live is torment;
and then have we a prescription to die, when death   305
is our physician.
Iago. O villainous! I have looked upon the world for
four times seven years, and since I could distinguish
betwixt a benefit and an injury, I never found man
that knew how to love himself. Ere I would say I   310
would drown myself for the love of a guinea hen, I
would change my humanity with a baboon.
Roderigo. What should I do? I confess it is my shame
to be so fond, but it is not in my virtue° to amend it.

---

293. **advantage:** opportunity.
301. **incontinently:** immediately.
314. **virtue:** nature.

Iago. Virtue! A fig! 'Tis in ourselves that we are thus, or   315
thus. Our bodies are our gardens, to the which our
wills are gardeners; so that if we will plant nettles or
sow lettuce, set hyssop and weed up thyme, supply it
with one gender° of herbs or distract° it with many—
either to have it sterile with idleness or manured with   320
industry—why, the power and corrigible authority°
of this lies in our wills. If the balance of our lives had
not one scale of reason to poise another of sensuality,
the blood° and baseness of our natures would
conduct us to most prepost'rous conclusions. But we   325
have reason to cool our raging motions, our carnal
stings, our unbitted° lusts, whereof I take this that
you call love to be a sect or scion.°

Roderigo. It cannot be.

Iago. It is merely a lust of the blood and a permission of   330
the will. Come, be a man. Drown thyself? Drown cats
and blind puppies! I have professed me thy friend,
and I confess me knit to thy deserving with cables of
perdurable° toughness. I could never better stead°
thee than now. Put money in thy purse. Follow thou   335
these wars; defeat thy favor° with an usurped° beard.
I say, put money in thy purse. It cannot be that
Desdemona should long continue her love of the
Moor. Put money in thy purse. Nor he his to her. It
was a violent commencement in her and thou shalt   340
see an answerable sequestration°—put but money in
thy purse. These Moors are changeable in their wills—
fill thy purse with money. The food that to him now is

---

319. **gender:** kind. **distract:** divide; diversify.
321. **corrigible authority:** power to correct.
324. **blood:** natural passions.
327. **unbitted:** uncontrolled.
328. **sect or scion:** offshoot or offspring.
334. **perdurable:** very durable. **stead:** assist.
336. **defeat thy favor:** disguise your face. **usurped:** false.
341. **answerable sequestration:** similar separation.

as luscious as locusts° shall be to him shortly as bitter
as coloquintida.° She must change for youth; when   345
she is sated with his body, she will find the error of
her choice. Therefore, put money in thy purse. If thou
wilt needs damn thyself, do it a more delicate way
than drowning. Make all the money thou canst. If
sanctimony° and a frail vow betwixt an erring°   350
barbarian and a supersubtle Venetian be not too hard
for my wits and all the tribe of hell, thou shalt enjoy
her. Therefore, make money. A pox of drowning
thyself! It is clean out of the way. Seek thou rather to
be hanged in compassing° thy joy than to be drowned   355
and go without her.

Roderigo. Wilt thou be fast to my hopes, if I depend on
the issue?

Iago. Thou art sure of me. Go, make money. I have told
thee often, and I retell thee again and again, I hate the   360
Moor. My cause is hearted;° thine hath no less reason.
Let us be conjunctive° in our revenge against him. If
thou canst cuckold him, thou dost thyself a pleasure,
me a sport. There are many events in the womb of
time which will be delivered. Traverse!° Go, provide   365
thy money. We will have more of this tomorrow.
Adieu.

Roderigo. Where shall we meet i' th' morning?

Iago. At my lodging.

Roderigo. I'll be with thee betimes.   370

Iago. Go to; farewell. Do you hear, Roderigo?

Roderigo. What say you?

Iago. No more of drowning, do you hear?

---

344. **locusts:** (probably) fruit of the carob tree.
345. **coloquintida:** bitter apple, used as a laxative.
350. **sanctimony:** sacred ceremony (of marriage). **erring:** wandering.
355. **compassing:** achieving.
361. **hearted:** deeply felt.
362. **conjunctive:** united; allied.
365. **Traverse!:** military order for troops to move.

Roderigo. I am changed: I'll sell all my land.　　[*Exit.*]
Iago.

    Thus do I ever make my fool my purse;　　　　　375
    For I mine own gained knowledge° should profane
    If I would time expend with such a snipe
    But for my sport and profit. I hate the Moor,
    And it is thought abroad° that 'twixt my sheets
    H' as done my office. I know not if't be true,　　　380
    But I, for mere suspicion in that kind,
    Will do, as if for surety.° He holds me well;
    The better shall my purpose work on him.
    Cassio's a proper° man. Let me see now:
    To get his place, and to plume up° my will　　　385
    In double knavery. How? How? Let's see.
    After some time, to abuse° Othello's ear
    That he is too familiar with his wife.
    He hath a person and a smooth dispose°
    To be suspected—framed to make women false.　　390
    The Moor is of a free and open nature
    That thinks men honest that but seem to be so;
    And will as tenderly° be led by th' nose
    As asses are.
    I have't! It is engendered! Hell and night　　　395
    Must bring this monstrous birth to the world's light.
　　　　　　　　　　　　　　　　　　　　Exit.

---

376. **gained knowledge:** practical wisdom.
379. **thought abroad:** rumored.
382. **surety:** certainty.
384. **proper:** handsome.
385. **plume up:** glorify.
387. **abuse:** deceive.
389. **dispose:** manner.
393. **tenderly:** easily.

Act II

Scene 1. *A seaport in Cyprus. An open place near the quay.*

Enter MONTANO *and two* GENTLEMEN.

Montano.
　　What from the cape can you discern at sea?
First Gentleman.
　　Nothing at all, it is a high-wrought flood.°
　　I cannot 'twixt the heaven and the main
　　Descry a sail.
Montano.
　　Methinks the wind hath spoke aloud at land;　　　　5
　　A fuller blast ne'er shook our battlements.
　　If it hath ruffianed so upon the sea,
　　What ribs of oak, when mountains melt on them,
　　Can hold the mortise?° What shall we hear of this?
Second Gentleman.
　　A segregation° of the Turkish fleet:　　　　　　　10
　　For do but stand upon the foaming shore,
　　The chidden° billow seems to pelt the clouds;
　　The wind-shaked surge, with high and monstrous
　　　　mane,
　　Seems to cast water on the burning Bear
　　And quench the guards of th' ever-fixèd pole.°　　15

II.1.2.　**high-wrought flood:** very angry sea.
　　9.　**hold the mortise:** hold their joints together.
　10.　**segregation:** separated part.
　12.　**chidden:** repelled (by the shore).
14–15.　**Seems . . . pole:** The bear (constellation Ursa Minor) contains two
　　　　bright stars that were said to be the guards of the pole (North Star).

I never did like molestation° view
On the enchafèd flood.°
Montano.   If that the Turkish fleet
Be not ensheltered and embayed, they are drowned;
It is impossible to bear it out.

Enter a third GENTLEMAN.

Third Gentleman.
News, lads! our wars are done.   20
The desperate tempest hath so banged the Turks
That their designment° halts. A noble ship of Venice
Hath seen a grievous wreck and sufferance°
On most part of their fleet.
Montano.
How? Is this true?
Third Gentleman.   The ship is here put in,   25
A Veronesa; Michael Cassio,
Lieutenant to the warlike Moor Othello,
Is come on shore; the Moor himself at sea,
And is in full commission here for Cyprus.
Montano.
I am glad on't. 'Tis a worthy governor.   30
Third Gentleman.
But this same Cassio, though he speak of comfort
Touching the Turkish loss, yet he looks sadly°
And prays the Moor be safe, for they were parted
With foul and violent tempest.
Montano.   Pray heavens he be;
For I have served him, and the man commands   35
Like a full° soldier. Let's to the seaside, ho!
As well to see the vessel that's come in

---

16. **like molestation:** similar uproar.
17. **enchafèd flood:** angry sea.
22. **designment:** enterprise.
23. **sufferance:** damage.
32. **sadly:** gravely; seriously.
36. **full:** perfect.

As to throw out our eyes for brave Othello,
Even till we make the main and th' aerial blue
An indistinct regard.°
Third Gentleman.   Come, let's do so;   40
For every minute is expectancy
Of more arrivancie.°

Enter CASSIO.

Cassio.
Thanks, you the valiant of this warlike isle,
That so approve° the Moor. O, let the heavens
Give him defence against the elements,   45
For I have lost him on a dangerous sea.
Montano.
Is he well shipped?
Cassio.
His bark is stoutly timbered, and his pilot
Of very expert and approved allowance;°
Therefore my hopes, not surfeited to death,   50
Stand in bold cure.°

A cry within: "A sail, a sail, a sail!"

Enter a MESSENGER.

Cassio.
What noise?
Messenger.
The town is empty; on the brow o' th' sea
Stand ranks of people, and they cry, "A sail!"
Cassio.
My hopes do shape him for the governor.   55

39–40. the main . . . regard: the sea and sky become indistinguishable.
  42. arrivancie: people arriving.
  44. approve: honor.
  49. approved allowance: tested reputation.
50–51. my hopes . . . cure: my hopes are not overly optimistic but are
    likely to be fulfilled.

Guns are heard.

Second Gentlemen.
    They do discharge their shot of courtesy:
    Our friends at least.
Cassio.   I pray you, sir, go forth
    And give us truth who 'tis that is arrived.
Second Gentleman.
    I shall.   *[Exit.]*
Montano.
    But, good lieutenant, is your general wived?   60
Cassio.
    Most fortunately. He hath achieved a maid
    That paragons° description and wild fame;°
    One that excels the quirks° of blazoning pens,
    And in th' essential vesture of creation
    Does tire the ingener.°

Enter second GENTLEMAN.

                         How now! who has put in?   65
Second Gentleman.
    'Tis one Iago, ancient to the general.
Cassio.
    H'as had most favorable and happy speed:
    Tempests themselves, high seas, and howling winds,
    The guttered° rocks and congregated sands,
    Traitors ensteeped° to clog the guiltless keel,   70
    As having sense of beauty, do omit
    Their mortal° natures, letting go safely by
    The divine Desdemona.
Montano.   What is she?

---

62. **paragons:** surpasses. **wild fame:** extravagant report.
63. **quirks:** extravagant conceits.
64–65. **in th' essential . . . ingener:** in the beauty of her form outstrips the
    imagination.
69. **guttered:** jagged.
70. **ensteeped:** submerged.
72. **mortal:** deadly.

Cassio.

> She that I spake of, our great captain's captain,
> Left in the conduct of the bold Iago,   75
> Whose footing° here anticipates our thoughts
> A se'nnight's° speed. Great Jove, Othello guard
> And swell his sail with thine own powerful breath,
> That he may bless this bay with his tall° ship,
> Make love's quick pants in Desdemona's arms,   80
> Give renewed fire to our extincted spirits,
> And bring all Cyprus comfort!

Enter DESDEMONA, EMILIA, IAGO, *and* RODERIGO.

>   O, behold,
> The riches of the ship is come on shore!
> You men of Cyprus, let her have your knees.

Kneels.

> Hail to thee, lady! And the grace of heaven,   85
> Before, behind thee, and on every hand,
> Enwheel° thee round!

Desdemona.   I thank you, valiant Cassio.

> What tidings can you tell me of my lord?

Cassio.

> He is not yet arrived; nor know I aught
> But that he's well and will be shortly here.   90

Desdemona.

> O, but I fear. How lost you company?

Cassio.

> The great contention of the sea and skies
> Parted our fellowship.

Within: "A sail, a sail!" *Guns are heard.*

>   But hark. A sail!

---

76. **footing:** landing.
77. **se'nnight's:** seven nights'; week's.
79. **tall:** brave; gallant.
87. **Enwheel:** encircle.

Second Gentleman.
    They give their greeting to the citadel;
    This likewise is a friend.

Cassio.   See for the news.   95

Exit SECOND GENTLEMAN.

    Good ancient, you are welcome. [*To* EMILIA.]
        Welcome, mistress.
    Let it not gall your patience, good Iago,
    That I extend° my manners. 'Tis my breeding
    That gives me this bold show of courtesy.

Kisses EMILIA.

Iago.
    Sir, would she give you so much of her lips   100
    As of her tongue she oft bestows on me,°
    You would have enough.

Desdemona. Alas, she has no speech.

Iago.   In faith, too much.
    I find it still° when I have list° to sleep.
    Marry, before your ladyship, I grant,   105
    She puts her tongue a little in her heart
    And chides with thinking.

Emilia.   You have little cause to say so.

Iago.
    Come on, come on! You are pictures out of doors,°
    Bells in your parlors, wildcats in your kitchens,
    Saints in your injuries,° devils being offended,   110
    Players° in your housewifery, and housewives in
        your beds.

---

  98. **extend:** stretch.
  101. **her tongue . . . me:** she often scolds me.
  104. **still:** always. **list:** desire.
  108. **pictures out of doors:** silent and well-behaved in public.
  110. **in your injuries:** when you injure others.
  111. **Players:** idlers.

Desdemona.

O, fie upon thee, slanderer!

Iago.

Nay, it is true, or else I am a Turk:

You rise to play, and go to bed to work.

Emilia.

You shall not write my praise.

Iago.   No, let me not.   115

Desdemona.

What wouldst thou write of me, if thou shouldst
    praise me?

Iago.

O gentle lady, do not put me to't,

For I am nothing if not critical.

Desdemona.

Come on, assay.° There's one gone to the harbor?

Iago.

Ay, madam.   120

Desdemona. [*Aside.*]

I am not merry; but I do beguile

The thing I am° by seeming otherwise.—

Come, how wouldst thou praise me?

Iago.

I am about it; but indeed my invention

Comes from my pate as bird lime° does from
    frieze°—   125

It plucks out brains and all. But my Muse labors,

And thus she is delivered:

If she be fair° and wise: fairness and wit,

The one's for use, the other useth it.

Desdemona.

Well praised! How if she be black° and witty?   130

---

119. **assay:** try.
122. **The thing I am:** my anxious self.
125. **bird lime:** sticky substance used to catch small birds. **frieze:** coarse
    woolen cloth.
128. **fair:** light-complexioned.
130. **black:** dark-complexioned.

Iago.

    If she be black, and thereto have a wit,

    She'll find a white that shall her blackness fit.

Desdemona.

    Worse and worse!

Emilia.   How if fair and foolish?

Iago.

    She never yet was foolish that was fair,

    For even her folly helped her to an heir.   135

Desdemona. These are old fond° paradoxes to make fools laugh i' th' alehouse. What miserable praise hast thou for her that's foul and foolish?

Iago.

    There's none so foul and foolish thereunto,

    But does foul pranks which fair and wise ones do.   140

Desdemona. O heavy ignorance! thou praisest the worst best. But what praise couldst thou bestow on a deserving woman indeed—one that in the authority of her merit did justly put on the vouch° of very malice itself?   145

Iago.

    She that was ever fair, and never proud;

    Had tongue at will, and yet was never loud;

    Never lacked gold, and yet went never gay;°

    Fled from her wish, and yet said "Now I may";

    She that being angered, her revenge being nigh,   150

    Bade her wrong stay, and her displeasure fly;

    She that in wisdom never was so frail

    To change the cod's head for the salmon's tail;°

    She that could think, and nev'r disclose her mind;

    See suitors following, and not look behind: 155

    She was a wight° (if ever such wights were)—

---

136. fond: foolish.

144. put on the vouch: compel the approval.

148. gay: extravagantly dressed.

153. change . . . tail: (perhaps) exchange something worthless for something more valuable.

156. wight: person.

Desdemona. To do what?

Iago.

To suckle fools and chronicle small beer.°

Desdemona. O most lame and impotent conclusion. Do
not learn of him, Emilia, though he be thy husband.   160
How say you, Cassio? Is he not a most profane° and
liberal° counselor?

Cassio. He speaks home,° madam. You may relish him
more in the soldier than in the scholar. [*Taking*
DESDEMONA*'s hand.*]

Iago. [*Aside.*] He takes her by the palm. Ay, well said,°   165
whisper! With as little a web as this will I ensnare as
great a fly as Cassio. Ay, smile upon her, do! I will
gyve° thee in thine own courtship.—You say true; 'tis
so, indeed!—If such tricks as these strip you out of
your lieutenantry, it had been better you had not   170
kissed your three fingers so oft—which now again
you are most apt to play the sir° in. Very good! Well
kissed! An excellent courtesy! 'Tis so, indeed. Yet
again your fingers to your lips? Would they were
clyster pipes° for your sake!   175

Trumpets within.

The Moor! I know his trumpet.°

Cassio.   'Tis truly so.

Desdemona. Let's meet him and receive him.

Cassio.   Lo, where he comes!

---

158. **chronicle small beer:** keep minor household accounts; that is, be
      concerned with trivial matters.
161. **profane:** irreverent; ribald.
162. **liberal:** licentious.
163. **home:** directly; on target.
165. **well said:** well done.
168. **gyve:** shackle; bind.
172. **sir:** fine gentleman.
175. **clyster pipes:** tubes used for enemas.
176. **trumpet:** (Commanders had distinctive calls.)

Enter OTHELLO *and* ATTENDANTS.

Othello.
    O my fair warrior!
Desdemona.   My dear Othello.
Othello.
    It gives me wonder great as my content
    To see you here before me. O my soul's joy!   180
    If after every tempest come such calms,
    May the winds blow till they have wakened death.
    And let the laboring bark climb hills of seas
    Olympus-high and duck again as low
    As hell's from heaven! If it were now to die,   185
    'Twere now to be most happy; for I fear
    My soul hath her content so absolute
    That not another comfort like to this
    Succeeds in unknown fate.
Desdemona.   The heavens forbid
    But that our loves and comforts should increase   190
    Even as our days do grow.
Othello.   Amen to that, sweet powers!
    I cannot speak enough of this content;
    It stops me here [*touching his heart*]; it is too much
       of joy.
    And this, and this, the greatest discords be

Kisses her.

    That e'er our hearts shall make!
Iago. [*Aside.*]   O, you are well tuned now!   195
    But I'll set down the pegs° that make this music,
    As honest as I am.
Othello.   Come, let us to the castle.
    News, friends! Our wars are done; the Turks are
       drowned.

---

196. set down the pegs: loosen the strings (and thereby untune the
    musical instrument).

How does my old acquaintance of this isle?
Honey, you shall be well desired in Cyprus;   200
I have found great love amongst them. O my sweet,
I prattle out of fashion, and I dote
In mine own comforts. I prithee, good Iago,
Go to the bay and disembark my coffers.
Bring thou the master° to the citadel;   205
He is a good one, and his worthiness
Does challenge° much respect. Come, Desdemona,
Once more well met at Cyprus.

> *Exeunt all but* IAGO *and* RODERIGO.

Iago. [*To an* ATTENDANT.] Do thou meet me presently at
the harbor. [*To* RODERIGO.] Come hither. If thou be'st   210
valiant (as they say base° men being in love have then
a nobility in their natures more than is native to them),
list me. The lieutenant tonight watches on the court
of guard.° First, I must tell thee this: Desdemona is
directly in love with him.   215
Roderigo. With him? Why, 'tis not possible.
Iago. Lay thy finger thus [*putting his finger to his lips*], and
let thy soul be instructed. Mark me with what
violence she first loved the Moor but° for bragging
and telling her fantastical lies. To love him still for   220
prating? Let not thy discreet heart think it. Her eye
must be fed. And what delight shall she have to look
on the devil? When the blood is made dull with the
act of sport, there should be a game to inflame it and
to give satiety a fresh appetite, loveliness in favor,°   225
sympathy° in years, manners, and beauties; all which
the Moor is defective in. Now for want of these
required conveniences, her delicate tenderness will

---

205. **master:** ship's captain.
207. **challenge:** deserve.
211. **base:** lowly born.
213–214. **court of guard:** guardhouse.
219. **but:** only.
225. **favor:** appearance.
226. **sympathy:** agreement.

find itself abused, begin to heave the gorge,° disrelish
and abhor the Moor. Very nature will instruct her in it   230
and compel her to some second choice. Now, sir, this
granted—as it is a most pregnant° and unforced
position—who stands so eminent in the degree of this
fortune as Cassio does? A knave very voluble; no
further conscionable° than in putting on the mere   235
form of civil and humane° seeming for the better
compass of his salt° and most hidden loose affection.
Why, none! Why, none! A slipper° and subtle knave, a
finder of occasion, that has an eye can stamp and
counterfeit advantages, though true advantage never   240
present itself. A devilish knave. Besides, the knave is
handsome, young, and hath all those requisites in
him that folly and green minds look after. A pestilent
complete knave, and the woman hath found him
already.   245

Roderigo. I cannot believe that in her; she's full of most
blessed condition.

Iago. Blessed fig's-end! The wine she drinks is made of
grapes. If she had been blessed, she would never
have loved the Moor. Blessed pudding!° Didst thou   250
not see her paddle with the palm of his hand? Didst
not mark that?

Roderigo. Yes, that I did; but that was but courtesy.

Iago. Lechery, by this hand! [*Extending his index finger.*]
An index° and obscure prologue to the history of   255
lust and foul thoughts. They met so near with their
lips that their breaths embraced together. Villainous
thoughts, Roderigo! When these mutualities° so

---

229. **heave the gorge:** feel nauseated; vomit.
232. **pregnant:** likely; cogent.
234–235. **no further conscionable:** having no more conscience.
236. **humane:** polite.
237. **salt:** lecherous.
238. **slipper:** slippery.
250. **pudding:** sausage.
255. **index:** pointer.
258. **mutualities:** reciprocal intimacies.

marshal the way, hard at hand comes the master and
main exercise, th' incorporate° conclusion: Pish! But,   260
sir, be you ruled by me. I have brought you from
Venice. Watch you tonight; for the command, I'll
lay't upon you. Cassio knows you not. I'll not be far
from you. Do you find some occasion to anger
Cassio, either by speaking too loud, or tainting° his   265
discipline; or from what other course you please
which the time shall more favorably minister.

Roderigo. Well.

Iago. Sir, he's rash and very sudden in choler,° and
haply may strike at you. Provoke him that he may;   270
for even out of that will I cause these of Cyprus to
mutiny, whose qualification shall come into no true
taste° again but by the displanting of Cassio. So
shall you have a shorter journey to your desires by
the means I shall then have to prefer them; and the   275
impediment most profitably removed without the
which there were no expectation of our prosperity.

Roderigo. I will do this if I can bring it to any opportunity.

Iago. I warrant thee. Meet me by and by at the citadel.
I must fetch his necessaries ashore. Farewell.   280

Roderigo. Adieu.   [*Exit.*]

Iago.

That Cassio loves her, I do well believe 't;
That she loves him, 'tis apt° and of great credit.°
The Moor, howbeit that I endure him not,
Is of a constant, loving, noble nature,   285
And I dare think he'll prove to Desdemona
A most dear° husband. Now I do love her too;
Not out of absolute lust, though peradventure
I stand accountant° for as great a sin,

---

260. **incorporate:** carnal; bodily.
265. **tainting:** disparaging.
269. **choler:** anger.
272–273. **qualification . . . taste:** appeasement shall not be attained.
283. **apt:** likely. **credit:** believability.
287. **dear:** costly.
289. **accountant:** accountable.

But partly led to diet° my revenge,   290
For that I do suspect the lusty Moor
Hath leaped into my seat; the thought whereof
Doth, like a poisonous mineral, gnaw my inwards;
And nothing can or shall content my soul
Till I am evened with him, wife for wife,   295
Or failing so, yet that I put the Moor
At least into a jealousy so strong
That judgment cannot cure. Which thing to do,
If this poor trash of Venice, whom I trace°
For his quick hunting, stand the putting on,   300
I'll have our Michael Cassio on the hip,
Abuse° him to the Moor in the rank garb°
(For I fear Cassio with my nightcap too),
Make the Moor thank me, love me, and reward me
For making him egregiously an ass   305
And practicing upon° his peace and quiet,
Even to madness. 'Tis here, but yet confused:
Knavery's plain face is never seen till used.   [*Exit.*]

Scene 2. *A street.*

Enter a HERALD *with a proclamation.*

Herald. It is Othello's pleasure, our noble and valiant
general, that upon certain tidings now arrived
importing the mere perdition° of the Turkish fleet,
every man put himself into triumph. Some to dance,
some to make bonfires, each man to what sport and   5
revels his addiction° leads him. For, besides these
beneficial news, it is the celebration of his nuptial. So

---

290. diet: indulge; feed.
299. trace: set on the track; train.
302. Abuse: slander. **rank garb:** coarse manner.
306. practicing upon: plotting against.
II.2.3. mere perdition: complete destruction; total loss.
  6. addiction: inclination.

much was his pleasure should be proclaimed. All
offices° are open, and there is full liberty of feasting
from this present hour of five till the bell have told   10
eleven. Heaven bless the isle of Cyprus and our
noble general Othello!   [*Exit.*]

Scene 3. *A hall in the castle.*

Enter OTHELLO, DESDEMONA, CASSIO, *and* ATTENDANTS.

Othello.
Good Michael, look you to the guard tonight.
Let's teach ourselves that honorable stop,
Not to outsport discretion.°
Cassio.
Iago hath direction what to do;
But notwithstanding, with my personal eye   5
Will I look to't.
Othello.   Iago is most honest.
Michael, good night. Tomorrow with your earliest
Let me have speech with you. [*To* DESDEMONA.]
    Come, my dear love,
The purchase made, the fruits are to ensue,
That profit's yet to come 'tween me and you.   10
Good night.

    Exeunt OTHELLO, DESDEMONA, *and* ATTENDANTS.

Enter IAGO.

Cassio. Welcome, Iago. We must to the watch.
Iago. Not this hour, lieutenant; 'tis not yet ten o' th'
clock. Our general cast° us thus early for the love of

---

   9. **offices:** rooms where food and drink are kept.
II.3.3. **outsport discretion:** celebrate to excess.
  14. **cast:** released; dismissed.

his Desdemona; who let us not therefore blame. He   15
hath not yet made wanton the night with her, and
she is sport for Jove.

Cassio. She's a most exquisite lady.

Iago. And, I'll warrant her, full of game.

Cassio. Indeed, she's a most fresh and delicate creature.   20

Iago. What an eye she has! Methinks it sounds a parley
to provocation.

Cassio. An inviting eye; and yet methinks right modest.

Iago. And when she speaks, is it not an alarum° to love?

Cassio. She is indeed perfection.   25

Iago. Well, happiness to their sheets! Come, lieutenant, I
have a stoup° of wine, and here without are a brace°
of Cyprus gallants that would fain have a measure to
the health of black Othello.

Cassio. Not tonight, good Iago. I have very poor and   30
unhappy brains for drinking; I could well wish courtesy
would invent some other custom of entertainment.

Iago. O, they are our friends. But one cup! I'll drink for
you.

Cassio. I have drunk but one cup tonight, and that was   35
craftily qualified° too; and behold what innovation
it makes here. I am unfortunate in the infirmity and
dare not task my weakness with any more.

Iago. What, man! 'Tis a night of revels, the gallants
desire it.   40

Cassio. Where are they?

Iago. Here, at the door. I pray you call them in.

Cassio. I'll do't, but it dislikes me.   [*Exit.*]

Iago.

If I can fasten but one cup upon him
With that which he hath drunk tonight already,   45
He'll be as full of quarrel and offense

---

24. **alarum:** call to arms.
27. **stoup:** two-quart tankard (cup). **brace:** pair.
36. **qualified:** diluted.

As my young mistress' dog. Now, my sick fool
    Roderigo,
Whom love hath turned almost the wrong side out,
To Desdemona hath tonight caroused
Potations pottle-deep;° and he's to watch.   50
Three else of Cyprus, noble swelling° spirits,
That hold their honors in a wary distance,°
The very elements of this warlike isle,
Have I tonight flustered with flowing cups,
And they watch too. Now, 'mongst this flock of
    drunkards   55
Am I to put our Cassio in some action
That may offend the isle. But here they come.

Enter CASSIO *with* MONTANO *and* GENTLEMEN, SERVANTS
following with wine.

If consequence do but approve my dream,
My boat sails freely, both with wind and stream.
Cassio. 'Fore God, they have given me a rouse° already.   60
Montano. Good faith, a little one; not past a pint, as I
  am a soldier.
Iago. Some wine, ho!

Sings.

   "And let me the canakin clink, clink;
   And let me the canakin clink.   65
      A soldier's a man;
      O man's life's but a span,
  Why then, let a soldier drink."

  Some wine, boys!
Cassio. 'Fore God, an excellent song!   70

---

50. **pottle-deep:** to the bottom of the tankard.
51. **swelling:** proud.
52. **hold . . . distance:** are very sensitive to insults to their honor.
60. **rouse:** large drink.

Iago. I learned it in England, where indeed, they are most potent in potting.° Your Dane, your German, and your swag-bellied Hollander—Drink, ho!—are nothing to your English.

Cassio. Is your Englishman so exquisite in his drinking?   75

Iago. Why, he drinks you with facility your Dane dead drunk; he sweats not to overthrow your Almain;° he gives your Hollander a vomit ere the next pottle can be filled.

Cassio. To the health of our general!   80

Montano. I am for it, lieutenant, and I'll do you justice.

Iago. O sweet England!

Sings.

> "King Stephen was and a worthy peer;
>   His breeches cost him but a crown;
> He held them sixpence all too dear,   85
>   With that he called the tailor lown.°

> "He was a wight of high renown,
>   And thou art but of low degree:
> 'Tis pride that pulls the country down;
>   Then take thine auld cloak about thee."   90

Some wine, ho!

Cassio. 'Fore God, this is a more exquisite song than the other.

Iago. Will you hear't again?

Cassio. No, for I hold him to be unworthy of his place   95
that does those things. Well, God's above all; and there be souls must be saved, and there be souls must not be saved.

Iago. It's true, good lieutenant.

---

72. **potting:** drinking.
77. **Almain:** German.
86. **lown:** lout; rascal.

Cassio. For mine own part—no offense to the general,   100
nor any man of quality—I hope to be saved.

Iago. And so do I too, lieutenant.

Cassio. Ay, but, by your leave, not before me. The
lieutenant is to be saved before the ancient. Let's
have no more of this; let's to our affairs.—God   105
forgive us our sins!—Gentlemen, let's look to our
business. Do not think, gentlemen, I am drunk. This
is my ancient; this is my right hand, and this is my
left. I am not drunk now. I can stand well enough,
and I speak well enough.   110

Gentlemen. Excellent well!

Cassio. Why, very well then. You must not think then
that I am drunk.   [*Exit.*]

Montano.
To th' platform, masters. Come, let's set the watch.

Iago.
You see this fellow that is gone before.   115
He is a soldier fit to stand by Caesar
And give direction; and do but see his vice.
'Tis to his virtue a just equinox,°
The one as long as th' other. 'Tis pity of him.
I fear the trust Othello puts him in,   120
On some odd time of his infirmity,
Will shake this island.

Montano.   But is he often thus?

Iago.
'Tis evermore his prologue to his sleep;
He'll watch the horologe a double set,°
If drink rock not his cradle.

Montano.   It were well   125
The general were put in mind of it.
Perhaps he sees it not, or his good nature
Prizes the virtue that appears in Cassio
And looks not on his evils. Is not this true?

---

118. **just equinox:** exact counterpart.
124. **watch . . . set:** remain awake twice around the clock (horologe).

Enter RODERIGO.

Iago. [*Aside.*]
    How now, Roderigo?   130
    I pray you after the lieutenant, go!

                                     Exit RODERIGO.

Montano.
    And 'tis great pity that the noble Moor
    Should hazard such a place as his own second
    With one of an ingraft° infirmity.
    It were an honest action to say so   135
    To the Moor.
Iago.   Not I, for this fair island!
    I do love Cassio well; and would do much
    To cure him of this evil.

Cry within: "Help! help!"

                        But hark! What noise?

Enter CASSIO *driving in* RODERIGO.

Cassio. Zounds, you rogue! You rascal!
Montano. What's the matter, lieutenant?   140
Cassio. A knave teach me my duty? I'll beat the knave
    into a twiggen° bottle.
Roderigo. Beat me?
Cassio. Dost thou prate, rogue?

Strikes RODERIGO.

Montano. Nay, good lieutenant! I pray you, sir, hold   145
    your hand.

Stays him.

Cassio. Let me go, sir, or I'll knock you o'er the mazzard.°

---

134. **ingraft:** deep-rooted.
142. **twiggen:** wicker-covered.
147. **mazzard:** head.

Montano. Come, come, you're drunk!
Cassio. Drunk?

They fight.

Iago. [*Aside to* RODERIGO.] Away, I say! Go out and cry   150
a mutiny!°

                                        Exit RODERIGO.

Nay, good lieutenant. God's will, gentlemen!
Help, ho! Lieutenant. Sir. Montano.
Help, masters! Here's a goodly watch indeed!

Bell rings.

Who's that which rings the bell! Diablo, ho!   155
The town will rise.° God's will, lieutenant,
You'll be ashamed forever.

Enter OTHELLO *and* ATTENDANTS.

Othello.   What is the matter here?
Montano.
Zounds, I bleed still. I am hurt to the death. He dies.

He and CASSIO *fight again.*

Othello.
Hold for your lives!
Iago.
Hold, ho! Lieutenant. Sir. Montano. Gentlemen!   160
Have you forgot all sense of place and duty?
Hold! The general speaks to you. Hold, for shame!
Othello.
Why, how now, ho? From whence ariseth this?
Are we turned Turks, and to ourselves do that
Which heaven hath forbid° the Ottomites?   165

---

151. **mutiny:** riot.
156. **rise:** grow riotous.
165. **forbid:** prevented.

For Christian shame put by this barbarous brawl!
He that stirs next to carve for his own rage
Holds his soul light;° he dies upon his motion.
Silence that dreadful bell! It frights the isle
From her propriety.° What is the matter, masters?   170
Honest Iago, that looks dead with grieving,
Speak. Who began this? On thy love, I charge thee.

Iago.

I do not know. Friends all, but now, even now,
In quarter° and in terms like bride and groom
Devesting them for bed; and then, but now—   175
As if some planet had unwitted men—
Swords out, and tilting one at other's breasts
In opposition bloody. I cannot speak
Any beginning to this peevish odds,°
And would in action glorious I had lost   180
Those legs that brought me to a part of it!

Othello.

How comes it, Michael, you are thus forgot?

Cassio.

I pray you pardon me; I cannot speak.

Othello.

Worthy Montano, you were wont be civil;
The gravity and stillness° of your youth   185
The world hath noted, and your name is great
In mouths of wisest censure.° What's the matter
That you unlace° your reputation thus
And spend your rich opinion for the name
Of a night-brawler? Give me answer to it.   190

---

168. **Holds his soul light:** places little value on his life.
170. **propriety:** proper order.
174. **quarter:** conduct.
179. **peevish odds:** senseless quarrel.
185. **stillness:** sober behavior.
187. **censure:** judgment.
188. **unlace:** undo; damage.

Montano.

> Worthy Othello, I am hurt to danger.
> Your officer, Iago, can inform you,
> While I spare speech, which something now
>   offends° me,
> Of all that I do know; nor know I aught
> By me that's said or done amiss this night,   195
> Unless self-charity be sometimes a vice,
> And to defend ourselves it be a sin
> When violence assails us.

Othello.   Now, by heaven,

> My blood° begins my safer guides to rule,
> And passion, having my best judgment collied,°   200
> Assays to lead the way. If I once stir
> Or do but lift this arm, the best of you
> Shall sink in my rebuke. Give me to know
> How this foul rout began, who set it on;
> And he that is approved in° this offense,   205
> Though he had twinned with me, both at a birth,
> Shall lose me. What? In a town of war
> Yet wild, the people's hearts brimful of fear,
> To manage° private and domestic quarrel?
> In night, and on the court and guard of safety?   210
> 'Tis monstrous. Iago, who began't?

Montano.

> If partially affined,° or leagued in office,
> Thou dost deliver more or less than truth,
> Thou art no soldier.

Iago.   Touch me not so near.

> I had rather have this tongue cut from my mouth   215
> Than it should do offense to Michael Cassio.

---

193. **offends:** hurts.
199. **blood:** anger.
200. **collied:** darkened.
205. **approved in:** found guilty of.
209. **manage:** carry on.
212. **partially affined:** made partial by a personal relationship.

Yet I persuade myself to speak the truth
Shall nothing wrong him. Thus it is, general.
Montano and myself being in speech,
There comes a fellow crying out for help,   220
And Cassio following him with determined sword
To execute upon him. Sir, this gentleman
Steps in to Cassio and entreats his pause.
Myself the crying fellow did pursue,
Lest by his clamor—as it so fell out—   225
The town might fall in fright. He, swift of foot,
Outran my purpose; and I returned then rather°
For that I heard the clink and fall of swords,
And Cassio high in oath; which till tonight
I ne'er might say before. When I came back—   230
For this was brief—I found them close together
At blow and thrust, even as again they were
When you yourself did part them.
More of this matter cannot I report;
But men are men; the best sometimes forget.°   235
Though Cassio did some little wrong to him,
As men in rage strike those that wish them best,
Yet surely Cassio, I believe, received
From him that fled some strange indignity,
Which patience could not pass.°
Othello.   I know, Iago,   240
Thy honesty and love doth mince this matter,
Making it light to Cassio. Cassio, I love thee;
But never more be officer of mine.

Enter DESDEMONA, *attended.*

Look if my gentle love be not raised up.
I'll make thee an example.
Desdemona.   What's the matter, dear?   245

---

227. **rather:** sooner.
235. **forget:** that is, forget themselves.
240. **pass:** overlook.

Othello.

　All's well now, sweeting; come away to bed.

To MONTANO.

　Sir, for your hurts, myself will be your surgeon.°
　Lead him off.

MONTANO is led off.

　Iago, look with care about the town,
　And silence those whom this vile brawl distracted.　　250
　Come, Desdemona; 'tis the soldiers' life
　To have their balmy slumbers waked with strife.

Exeunt all but IAGO and CASSIO.

Iago. What, are you hurt, lieutenant?

Cassio. Ay, past all surgery.

Iago. Marry, God forbid!　　　　　　　　　　　　255

Cassio. Reputation, reputation, reputation! O, I have lost my reputation! I have lost the immortal part of myself, and what remains is bestial. My reputation, Iago, my reputation.

Iago. As I am an honest man, I thought you had received　260 some bodily wound. There is more sense° in that than in reputation. Reputation is an idle and most false imposition,° oft got without merit and lost without deserving. You have lost no reputation at all unless you repute yourself such a loser. What, man, there are　265 ways to recover the general again. You are but now cast in his mood°—a punishment more in policy° than in malice—even so as one would beat his offenseless dog to affright an imperious lion. Sue to him again, and he's yours.　　　　　　　　　　　270

---

247. **myself . . . surgeon:** I will provide for your medical care.
261. **sense:** physical feeling.
263. **imposition:** external (therefore artificial) thing.
267. **cast in his mood:** dismissed in a moment of anger. **policy:** public (or political) gesture.

Cassio. I will rather sue to be despised than to deceive so
good a commander with so slight, so drunken, and so
indiscreet an officer. Drunk! And speak parrot!° And
squabble! Swagger! Swear! and discourse fustian°
with one's own shadow! O thou invisible spirit of   275
wine, if thou hast no name to be known by, let us call
thee devil!

Iago. What was he that you followed with your sword?
What had he done to you?

Cassio. I know not.   280

Iago. Is't possible?

Cassio. I remember a mass of things, but nothing
distinctly: a quarrel, but nothing wherefore. O God,
that men should put an enemy in their mouths to steal
away their brains! that we should with joy, pleasance,   285
revel, and applause transform ourselves into beasts!

Iago. Why, but you are now well enough. How came
you thus recovered?

Cassio. It hath pleased the devil drunkenness to give
place to the devil wrath. One unperfectness shows   290
me another, to make me frankly despise myself.

Iago. Come, you are too severe a moraler.° As the time,
the place, and the condition of this country stands, I
could heartily wish this had not befall'n; but since it
is as it is, mend it for your own good.   295

Cassio. I will ask him for my place again: he shall tell me
I am a drunkard. Had I as many mouths as Hydra,°
such an answer would stop them all. To be now a
sensible man, by and by a fool, and presently a beast!
O strange! Every inordinate cup is unblest, and the   300
ingredient is a devil.

---

273. **speak parrot:** talk without sense.
274. **discourse fustian:** talk nonsense.
292. **moraler:** moralizer.
297. **Hydra:** in Greek mythology, monster with many heads and the
ability to grow two heads when one was cut off; killed by Hercules.

Iago. Come, come, good wine is a good familiar°
    creature if it be well used. Exclaim no more against it.
    And, good lieutenant, I think you think I love you.

Cassio. I have well approved° it, sir. I drunk!   305

Iago. You or any man living may be drunk at a time,
    man. I tell you what you shall do. Our general's wife
    is now the general. I may say so in this respect, for
    that he hath devoted and given up himself to the
    contemplation, mark, and denotement° of her parts°   310
    and graces. Confess yourself freely to her; importune
    her help to put you in your place again. She is of so
    free,° so kind, so apt, so blessed a disposition she
    holds it a vice in her goodness not to do more than
    she is requested. This broken joint between you and   315
    her husband entreat her to splinter;° and my fortunes
    against any lay° worth naming, this crack of your
    love shall grow stronger than it was before.

Cassio. You advise me well.

Iago. I protest, in the sincerity of love and honest kindness.   320

Cassio. I think it freely; and betimes in the morning I will
    beseech the virtuous Desdemona to undertake for
    me. I am desperate of my fortunes if they check° me.

Iago. You are in the right. Good night, lieutenant; I
    must to the watch.   325

Cassio. Good night, honest Iago.   *[Exit.]*

Iago.
    And what's he then that says I play the villain,
    When this advice is free I give, and honest,
    Probal° to thinking, and indeed the course

---

302. familiar: friendly.
305. approved: proved.
310. mark, and denotement: (both) observation. **parts:** qualities.
313. free: generous.
316. splinter: bind with a splint.
317. lay: wager.
323. check: repulse.
329. Probal: probable; reasonable.

To win the Moor again? For 'tis most easy   330
Th' inclining° Desdemona to subdue
In any honest suit; she's framed as fruitful°
As the free elements.° And then for her
To win the Moor—were't to renounce his baptism,
All seals and symbols of redeemèd sin—   335
His soul is so enfettered to her love
That she may make, unmake, do what she list,
Even as her appetite shall play the god
With his weak function. How am I then a villain
To counsel Cassio to this parallel course,   340
Directly to his good? Divinity of hell!
When devils will the blackest sins put on,°
They do suggest at first with heavenly shows,
As I do now. For whiles this honest fool
Plies Desdemona to repair his fortune,   345
And she for him pleads strongly to the Moor,
I'll pour this pestilence into his ear:
That she repeals him° for her body's lust;
And by how much she strives to do him good,
She shall undo her credit with the Moor.   350
So will I turn her virtue into pitch,
And out of her own goodness make the net
That shall enmesh them all. How now, Roderigo?

Enter RODERIGO.

Roderigo. I do follow here in the chase, not like a hound
that hunts, but one that fills up the cry.° My money is   355
almost spent; I have been tonight exceedingly well
cudgeled; and I think the issue will be, I shall have so

---

331. **inclining:** favorably disposed.
332. **framed as fruitful:** created as generous.
333. **free elements:** natural elements or forces.
342. **put on:** further; advance.
348. **repeals him:** attempts to have Cassio reinstated.
355. **fills up the cry:** is merely one of the pack, making noise but not really
tracking.

much° experience for my pains, and so, with no
money at all, and a little more wit,° return again to
Venice.   360

Iago.

How poor are they that have not patience!
What wound did ever heal but by degrees?
Thou know'st we work by wit, and not by witchcraft;
And wit depends on dilatory time.
Does't not go well? Cassio hath beaten thee.   365
And thou by that small hurt hast cashiered Cassio.
Though other things grow fair against the sun,
Yet fruits that blossom first will first be ripe.
Content thyself awhile. By the mass, 'tis morning!
Pleasure and action make the hours seem short.   370
Retire thee; go where thou art billeted.
Away, I say! Thou shalt know more hereafter.
Nay, get thee gone.

                                                                      Exit RODERIGO.

                    Two things are to be done:
My wife must move° for Cassio to her mistress;
I'll set her on;   375
Myself awhile to draw the Moor apart
And bring him jump° when he may Cassio find
Soliciting his wife. Ay, that's the way!
Dull not device by coldness and delay.   [*Exit.*]

357–358. so much: just so much and not more.
359. wit: intelligence.
374. move: plead.
377. jump: exactly at the moment.

Act III

Scene 1. *Cyprus. Before the castle.*

Enter CASSIO *and some* MUSICIANS.

Cassio.
Masters, play here. I will content your pains.°
Something that's brief; and bid "Good morrow,
    general."

Music.

Enter CLOWN.

Clown. Why masters, have your instruments been in
    Naples,° that they speak i' th' nose thus?
Musician. How, sir, how?   5
Clown. Are these, I pray you, wind instruments?
Musician. Ay, marry, are they, sir.
Clown. O, thereby hangs a tail.
Musician. Whereby hangs a tale, sir?
Clown. Marry, sir, by many a wind instrument that I   10
    know. But, masters, here's money for you; and the
    general so likes your music that he desires you, for
    love's sake, to make no more noise with it.
Musician. Well, sir, we will not.
Clown. If you have any music that may not° be heard,   15
    to't again. But, as they say, to hear music the general
    does not greatly care.

III.1.1. **content your pains:** reward your efforts.
  4. Naples: (The reference might be to the Neapolitan accent or to
     venereal disease—supposedly rife in Naples—which attacks the
     nose.)
 15. may not: cannot.

Musician. We have none such, sir.

Clown. Then put up your pipes in your bag, for I'll
    away. Go, vanish into air, away! 20

Exeunt MUSICIANS.

Cassio. Dost thou hear, mine honest friend?

Clown. No, I hear not your honest friend. I hear you.

Cassio. Prithee, keep up thy quillets.° There's a poor piece
    of gold for thee. If the gentlewoman that attends the
    general's wife be stirring, tell her there's one Cassio 25
    entreats her a little favor of speech. Wilt thou do this?

Clown. She is stirring, sir: if she will stir hither, I shall
    seem° to notify unto her.   [*Exit.*]

Enter IAGO.

Cassio.
    In happy time, Iago.

Iago.   You have not been abed, then?

Cassio.
    Why no, the day had broke before we parted. 30
    I have made bold, Iago, to send in to your wife;
    My suit to her is that she will to virtuous Desdemona
    Procure me some access.

Iago.   I'll send her to you presently,
    And I'll devise a mean to draw the Moor
    Out of the way, that your converse and business 35
    May be more free.

Cassio.   I humbly thank you for't.

Exit IAGO.

    I never knew a Florentine° more kind and honest.

---

    23. **quillets:** puns; quibbles.
    28. **seem:** think fit; arrange.
    37. **Florentine:** one who lives in Florence. Cassio is from Florence, Iago
    from Venice.

Enter EMILIA.

Emilia.

Good morrow, good lieutenant: I am sorry
For your displeasure;° but all will sure be well.
The general and his wife are talking of it,   40
And she speaks for you stoutly. The Moor replies
That he you hurt is of great fame in Cyprus
And great affinity,° and that in wholesome wisdom
He might not but refuse you. But he protests he
    loves you,
And needs no other suitor but his likings   45
To take the safest occasion by the front°
To bring you in again.

Cassio.   Yet I beseech you,
If you think fit, or that it may be done,
Give me advantage of some brief discourse
With Desdemona alone.

Emilia.   Pray you come in.   50
I will bestow you where you shall have time
To speak your bosom° freely.

Cassio.   I am much bound to you.

                                        Exeunt.

Scene 2. *A room in the castle.*

Enter OTHELLO, IAGO, *and* GENTLEMEN.

Othello.

These letters give, Iago, to the pilot
And by him do my duties° to the Senate.

---

39. **displeasure:** being out of favor.
43. **affinity:** family connections.
46. **front:** forehead or forelock.
52. **bosom:** innermost thoughts and feelings.
III.2.2.   **do my duties:** pay my respects.

That done, I will be walking on the works;°
Repair° there to me.

Iago.   Well, my good lord, I'll do't.

Othello.

This fortification, gentlemen, shall we see't?   5

Gentlemen.

We'll wait upon° your lordship.

Exeunt.

Scene 3. *The garden of the castle.*

Enter DESDEMONA, CASSIO, *and* EMILIA.

Desdemona.

Be thou assured, good Cassio, I will do
All my abilities in thy behalf.

Emilia.

Good madam, do. I warrant it grieves my husband
As if the cause were his.

Desdemona.

O, that's an honest fellow. Do not doubt, Cassio,   5
But I will have my lord and you again
As friendly as you were.

Cassio.   Bounteous madam,
Whatever shall become of Michael Cassio,
He's never anything but your true servant.

Desdemona.

I know't; I thank you. You do love my lord.   10
You have known him long, and be you well assured
He shall in strangeness° stand no farther off
Than in a politic° distance.

Cassio.   Ay, but, lady,

---

3. **works:** fortifications.
4. **Repair:** return.
6. **wait upon:** attend.
III.3.12. **strangeness:** estrangement; aloofness.
13. **politic:** politically necessary; expedient.

That policy may either last so long,
Or feed upon such nice° and waterish diet,   15
Or breed itself so out of circumstances,°
That, I being absent and my place supplied,°
My general will forget my love and service.

Desdemona.

Do not doubt° that; before Emilia here
I give thee warrant of thy place. Assure thee,   20
If I do vow a friendship, I'll perform it
To the last article. My lord shall never rest;
I'll watch him tame° and talk him out of patience;
His bed shall seem a school, his board a shrift;°
I'll intermingle everything he does   25
With Cassio's suit: therefore be merry, Cassio,
For thy solicitor° shall rather die
Than give thy cause away.

Enter OTHELLO *and* IAGO *at a distance.*

Emilia.

Madam, here comes my lord.

Cassio.

Madam, I'll take my leave.   30

Desdemona.

Why, stay, and hear me speak.

Cassio.

Madam, not now. I am very ill at ease,
Unfit for mine own purposes.

Desdemona.

Well, do your discretion.

Exit CASSIO.

---

15. **nice:** thin; trivial.
16. **breed . . . circumstances:** (perhaps) produce so few opportunities for
    my reinstatement.
17. **supplied:** filled.
19. **doubt:** fear.
23. **watch him tame:** keep him awake in order to tame him. (Young
    hawks were so trained in falconry.)
24. **board a shrift:** table (shall seem) a confessional.
27. **solicitor:** advocate.

Iago.

Ha! I like not that.

Othello.   What dost thou say?   35

Iago.

Nothing, my lord; or if—I know not what.

Othello.

Was not that Cassio parted from my wife?

Iago.

Cassio, my lord! No, sure, I cannot think it,

That he would steal away so guilty-like,

Seeing you coming.

Othello.   I do believe 'twas he.   40

Desdemona. [*Approaching them.*]

How now, my lord?

I have been talking with a suitor here,

A man that languishes in your displeasure.

Othello.

Who is't you mean?

Desdemona.

Why, your lieutenant, Cassio. Good my lord,   45

If I have any grace or power to move you,

His present° reconciliation take.

For if he be not one that truly loves you,

That errs in ignorance, and not in cunning,°

I have no judgment in an honest face.   50

I prithee, call him back.

Othello.   Went he hence now?

Desdemona.

I' sooth so humbled

That he hath left part of his grief with me

To suffer with him. Good love, call him back.

Othello.

Not now, sweet Desdemon; some other time.   55

---

47. **present:** immediate.
49. **in cunning:** knowingly.

Desdemona.

But shall't be shortly?

Othello.   The sooner, sweet, for you.

Desdemona.

Shall't be tonight at supper?

Othello.   No, not tonight.

Desdemona.

Tomorrow dinner,° then?

Othello.   I shall not dine at home;

I meet the captains at the citadel.

Desdemona.

Why, then, tomorrow night, on Tuesday morn,   60
On Tuesday noon, or night; on Wednesday morn.
I prithee name the time, but let it not
Exceed three days. In faith, he's penitent;
And yet his trespass, in our common reason
(Save that, they say, the wars must make examples   65
Out of her best), is not almost° a fault
T' incur a private check.° When shall he come?
Tell me, Othello. I wonder in my soul
What you would ask me that I should deny
Or stand so mamm'ring on.° What? Michael Cassio,   70
That came awooing with you, and so many a time,
When I have spoke of you dispraisingly,
Hath ta'en your part—to have so much to do
To bring him in?° By'r Lady, I could do much—

Othello.

Prithee no more. Let him come when he will!   75
I will deny thee nothing.

Desdemona.   Why, this is not a boon;

'Tis as I should entreat you wear your gloves,
Or feed on nourishing dishes, or keep you warm,

---

58. **dinner:** midday meal.
66. **not almost:** scarcely; hardly.
67. **check:** reprimand.
70. **mamm'ring on:** hesitating.
74. **bring him in:** restore him to favor.

Or sue to you to do a peculiar° profit
To your own person. Nay, when I have a suit   80
Wherein I mean to touch your love indeed,
It shall be full of poise° and difficult weight,
And fearful to be granted.

Othello.   I will deny thee nothing!
Whereon I do beseech thee grant me this,
To leave me but a little to myself.   85

Desdemona.
Shall I deny you? No. Farewell, my lord.

Othello.
Farewell, my Desdemona: I'll come to thee straight.°

Desdemona.
Emilia, come. Be as your fancies° teach you;
Whate'er you be, I am obedient.

Exeunt DESDEMONA *and* EMILIA.

Othello.
Excellent wretch!° Perdition catch my soul   90
But I do° love thee! and when I love thee not,
Chaos is come again.

Iago.
My noble lord—

Othello.   What dost thou say, Iago?

Iago.
Did Michael Cassio, when you wooed my lady,
Know of your love?   95

Othello.
He did, from first to last. Why dost thou ask?

Iago.
But for a satisfaction of my thought,
No further harm.

---

79. **peculiar:** particular; personal.
82. **poise:** heaviness; importance.
87. **straight:** at once.
88. **fancies:** inclinations.
90. **wretch:** (term of endearment).
91. **But I do:** if I do not.

Othello.   Why of thy thought, Iago?
Iago.
   I did not think he had been acquainted with her.
Othello.
   O, yes, and went between us° very oft.   100
Iago.
   Indeed?
Othello.
   Indeed? Ay, indeed! Discern'st thou aught in that?
   Is he not honest?
Iago.   Honest, my lord?
Othello.   Honest? Ay, honest.
Iago.
   My lord, for aught I know.
Othello.
   What dost thou think?
Iago.   Think, my lord?
Othello.   Think, my lord?   105
   By heaven, thou echoest me,
   As if there were some monster in thy thought
   Too hideous to be shown. Thou dost mean something.
   I heard thee say even now, thou lik'st not that,
   When Cassio left my wife. What didst not like?   110
   And when I told thee he was of my counsel°
   In my whole course of wooing, thou crie'st, "Indeed?"
   And didst contract and purse thy brow together,
   As if thou then hadst shut up in thy brain
   Some horrible conceit.° If thou dost love me,   115
   Show me thy thought.
Iago.
   My lord, you know I love you.
Othello.   I think thou dost;
   And, for I know thou'rt full of love and honesty

---

100. **went between us:** was our messenger.
111. **of my counsel:** in my confidence.
115. **conceit:** idea; thought.

And weigh'st thy words before thou giv'st them
   breath,
Therefore these stops° of thine fright me the more;   120
For such things in a false disloyal knave
Are tricks of custom;° but in a man that's just
They're close dilations,° working from the heart
That passion cannot rule.

Iago.   For Michael Cassio,
I dare be sworn, I think that he is honest.   125

Othello.
I think so too.

Iago.   Men should be what they seem;
Or those that be not, would they might seem none!°

Othello.
Certain, men should be what they seem.

Iago.
Why then, I think Cassio's an honest man.

Othello.
Nay, yet there's more in this?   130
I prithee speak to me as to thy thinkings,
As thou dost ruminate, and give thy worst of thoughts
The worst of words.

Iago.   Good my lord, pardon me:
Though I am bound to every act of duty,
I am not bound to that° all slaves are free to.   135
Utter my thoughts? Why, say they are vile and false,
As where's that palace whereinto foul things
Sometimes intrude not? Who has that breast so pure
But some uncleanly apprehensions°

---

120. **stops:** pauses.
122. **tricks of custom:** customary ploys.
123. **close dilations:** (The meaning is not clear; the phrase probably means
     either "expressions of hidden thoughts" or "involuntary delays.")
127. **none:** not to be men, or not to be honest men.
135. **that:** that which.
139. **apprehensions:** ideas.

Keep leets and law days,° and in session sit 140
With meditations lawful?

Othello.

Thou dost conspire against thy friend, Iago,
If thou but think'st him wronged, and mak'st his ear
A stranger to thy thoughts.

Iago.   I do beseech you—
Though I perchance am vicious° in my guess, 145
As I confess it is my nature's plague
To spy into abuses, and of my jealousy°
Shapes faults that are not—that your wisdom then,
From one that so imperfectly conceits°
Would take no notice, nor build yourself a trouble 150
Out of his scattering° and unsure observance.
It were not for your quiet nor your good,
Nor for my manhood, honesty, or wisdom,
To let you know my thoughts.

Othello.   What dost thou mean?

Iago.

Good name in man and woman, dear my lord, 155
Is the immediate° jewel of their souls.
Who steals my purse steals trash;° 'tis something,
     nothing;
'Twas mine, 'tis his, and has been slave to
     thousands;
But he that filches from me my good name
Robs me of that which not enriches him 160
And makes me poor indeed.

Othello.

By heaven, I'll know thy thoughts!

---

140. **Keep . . . days:** hold meetings of local courts.
145. **vicious:** wrong.
147. **jealousy:** suspicion of evil.
149. **conceits:** conjectures; judges.
151. **scattering:** random.
156. **immediate:** most important.
157. **trash:** (scornful term for) money.

Iago.

You cannot, if my heart were in your hand;
Nor shall not whilst 'tis in my custody.

Othello.

Ha!

Iago.   O, beware, my lord, of jealousy!   165
It is the green-eyed monster which doth mock
The meat it feeds on.° That cuckold lives in bliss
Who, certain of his fate, loves not his wronger;°
But O, what damnèd minutes tells° he o'er
Who dotes, yet doubts—suspects, yet fondly° loves!   170

Othello.

O misery.

Iago.

Poor and content is rich, and rich enough;
But riches fineless° is as poor as winter
To him that ever fears he shall be poor.
Good God the souls of all my tribe defend   175
From jealousy!

Othello.   Why? Why is this?
Think'st thou I'd make a life of jealousy,
To follow still the changes of the moon
With fresh suspicions?° No! To be once in doubt
Is once° to be resolved.° Exchange me for a goat   180
When I shall turn the business of my soul
To such exsufflicate and blown° surmises,
Matching thy inference.° 'Tis not to make me jealous
To say my wife is fair, feeds well, loves company,

166–167.   doth . . . on: mocks and torments its victim, the jealous person.
168.   wronger: his unfaithful wife.
169.   tells: counts.
170.   fondly: foolishly.
173.   fineless: boundless; infinite.
178–179.   To . . . suspicions: to have new suspicions with each new phase
   of the moon.
180.   once: once and for all. **resolved:** free of doubt.
182.   exsufflicate and blown: inflated and rumored (or, possibly, flyblown
   or spoiled).
183.   inference: allegation; depiction.

Is free of speech, sings, plays, and dances well;   185
Where virtue is, these are more virtuous.
Nor from mine own weak merits will I draw
The smallest fear or doubt of her revolt,°
For she had eyes, and chose me. No, Iago;
I'll see before I doubt; when I doubt, prove;   190
And on the proof there is no more but this:
Away at once with love or jealousy!

Iago.

I am glad of this; for now I shall have reason
To show the love and duty that I bear you
With franker spirit. Therefore, as I am bound,   195
Receive it from me. I speak not yet of proof.
Look to your wife; observe her well with Cassio;
Wear your eyes thus: not° jealous nor secure.°
I would not have your free and noble nature
Out of self-bounty° be abused.° Look to't.   200
I know our country disposition well:
In Venice they do let heaven see the pranks
They dare not show their husbands; their best
        conscience°
Is not to leave't undone, but kept unknown.

Othello.

Dost thou say so?   205

Iago.

She did deceive her father, marrying you;
And when she seemed to shake and fear your looks,
She loved them most.

Othello.   And so she did.

Iago.   Why, go to then!
She that so young could give out such a seeming°
To seel° her father's eyes up close as oak°—   210

---

188. **doubt of her revolt:** suspicion of her unfaithfulness.
198. **not:** neither. **secure:** free from suspicion.
200. **self-bounty:** innate goodness. **abused:** deceived.
203. **best conscience:** highest idea of morality.
209. **seeming:** false appearance.
210. **seel:** blind (term from falconry). **oak:** close-grained wood.

He thought 'twas witchcraft. But I am much to blame.
I humbly do beseech you of your pardon
For too much loving you.

Othello.   I am bound° to thee forever.

Iago.

I see this hath a little dashed your spirits.

Othello.

Not a jot, not a jot.

Iago.   I' faith, I fear it has.   215
I hope you will consider what is spoke
Comes from my love. But I do see y' are moved.
I am to pray you not to strain° my speech
To grosser issues, nor to larger reach°
Than to suspicion.   220

Othello.

I will not.

Iago.   Should you do so, my lord,
My speech should fall into such vile success°
As my thoughts aimed not. Cassio's my worthy
     friend—
My lord, I see y' are moved.

Othello.   No, not much moved.
I do not think but Desdemona's honest.°   225

Iago.

Long live she so! And long live you to think so.

Othello.

And yet, how nature erring from itself—

Iago.

Ay, there's the point, as (to be bold with you)
Not to affect° many proposèd matches
Of her own clime, complexion, and degree,°   230
Whereto we see in all things nature tends—

---

213. **bound:** indebted.
218. **strain:** exaggerate.
219. **reach:** meaning.
222. **success:** result.
225. **honest:** chaste; virtuous.
229. **affect:** like; prefer.
230. **degree:** social level.

Foh! one may smell in such a will most rank,
Foul disproportions, thoughts unnatural.
But, pardon me, I do not in position°
Distinctly speak of her; though I may fear   235
Her will, recoiling° to her better judgment,
May fall to match° you with her country forms,
And happily° repent.

Othello.   Farewell, farewell!
If more thou dost perceive, let me know more.
Set on thy wife to observe. Leave me, Iago.   240

Iago. [*Going.*]
My lord, I take my leave.

Othello.
Why did I marry? This honest creature doubtless
Sees and knows more, much more, than he unfolds.

Iago. [*Returning.*]
My lord, I would I might entreat your honor
To scan° this thing no farther. Leave it to time.   245
Although 'tis fit that Cassio have his place,
For sure he fills it up with great ability,
Yet, if you please to hold him off awhile,
You shall by that perceive him and his means.
Note if your lady strain his entertainment°   250
With any strong or vehement importunity;
Much will be seen in that. In the meantime
Let me be thought too busy° in my fears
As worthy cause I have to fear I am—
And hold her free,° I do beseech your honor.   255

Othello.
Fear not my government.°

---

234. **position:** general argument.
236. **recoiling:** reverting.
237. **fall to match:** happen to compare.
238. **happily:** by chance; perhaps.
245. **scan:** scrutinize.
250. **strain his entertainment:** urge his reinstatement.
253. **busy:** interfering.
255. **free:** innocent.
256. **government:** self-control.

Iago.   I once more take my leave.

                                                 Exit.

Othello.

    This fellow's of exceeding honesty,

    And knows all qualities,° with a learnèd spirit,

    Of human dealings. If I do prove her haggard,°

    Though that her jesses° were my dear heartstrings,   260

    I'd whistle her off and let her down the wind°

    To prey at fortune.° Haply, for° I am black

    And have not those soft parts of conversation°

    That chamberers° have, or for I am declined

    Into the vale of years—yet that's not much—   265

    She's gone. I am abused,° and my relief

    Must be to loathe her. O curse of marriage,

    That we can call these delicate creatures ours,

    And not their appetites! I had rather be a toad

    And live upon the vapor of a dungeon   270

    Than keep a corner in the thing I love

    For others' uses. Yet 'tis the plague to great ones;

    Prerogatived are they less than the base.°

    'Tis destiny unshunnable, like death.

    Even then this forkèd plague° is fated to us   275

    When we do quicken.° Look where she comes.

Enter DESDEMONA *and* EMILIA.

---

258. **qualities:** natures; types of people.
259. **haggard:** wild (like an untrained or wild hawk).
260. **jesses:** straps fastened to a trained hawk's legs (and then to a string around the falconer's wrist).
261. **I'd ... wind:** I'd release her and let her go free (like an untrainable hawk).
262. **prey at fortune:** fend for herself. **Haply, for:** perhaps because.
263. **soft parts of conversation:** pleasing social graces.
264. **chamberers:** gallants; (perhaps) seducers.
266. **abused:** deceived.
273. **Prerogatived ... base:** the privileged are less likely (to have honest wives) than ordinary men.
275. **forkèd plague:** curse of (a cuckold's) horns.
276. **do quicken:** are born.

If she be false, heaven mocks itself!
I'll not believe't.
Desdemona.　　　How now, my dear Othello?
　　Your dinner, and the generous° islanders
　　By you invited, do attend° your presence.　　　　　　280
Othello.
　　I am to blame.
Desdemona.　　Why do you speak so faintly?
　　Are you not well?
Othello.
　　I have a pain upon my forehead, here.°
Desdemona.
　　Why, that's with watching;° 'twill away again.
　　Let me but bind it hard, within this hour　　　　　　285
　　It will be well.
Othello.　　　Your napkin° is too little;

Pushes the handkerchief from him, and it drops.

　　Let it° alone. Come, I'll go in with you.
Desdemona.
　　I am very sorry that you are not well.

　　　　　　　　Exeunt OTHELLO *and* DESDEMONA.

Emilia.
　　I am glad I have found this napkin;
　　This was her first remembrance from the Moor.　　290
　　My wayward° husband hath a hundred times
　　Wooed me to steal it; but she so loves the token
　　(For he conjured her° she should ever keep it)

279.　**generous:** noble.
280.　**attend:** await.
283.　**here:** (that is, where his cuckold's horns would be).
284.　**watching:** lack of sleep.
286.　**napkin:** elaborate handkerchief.
287.　**it:** (refers either to the handkerchief or to Othello's forehead).
291.　**wayward:** capricious.
293.　**conjured her:** made her solemnly swear.

That she reserves it evermore about her
To kiss and talk to. I'll have the work ta'en out°   295
And give't Iago. What he will do with it,
Heaven knows, not I; I nothing but to please his
    fantasy.°

Enter IAGO.

Iago.
How now! What do you here alone?
Emilia.
Do not you chide; I have a thing for you.
Iago.
A thing for me? It is a common thing—   300
Emilia. Ha?
Iago.
To have a foolish wife.
Emilia.
O, is that all? What will you give me now
For the same handkerchief?
Iago.   What handkerchief?
Emilia.
What handkerchief!   305
Why, that the Moor first gave to Desdemona,
That which so often you did bid me steal.
Iago.
Hast stol'n it from her?
Emilia.
No, but she let it drop by negligence,
And to th' advantage,° I, being here, took't up.   310
Look, here 'tis.
Iago.   A good wench. Give it me.
Emilia.
What will you do with't, that you have been so
    earnest
To have me filch it?

---

295. **work ta'en out:** the design of the embroidery copied.
297. **fantasy:** whim.
310. **to th' advantage:** taking the opportunity; being lucky.

Iago. [*Snatching it.*]   Why, what is that to you?
Emilia.

If it be not for some purpose of import,
Give't me again. Poor lady, she'll run mad   315
When she shall lack it.
Iago.   Be not acknown on't.°
I have use for it. Go, leave me.

Exit EMILIA.

I will in Cassio's lodging lose this napkin
And let him find it. Trifles light as air
Are to the jealous confirmations strong   320
As proofs of Holy Writ. This may do something.
The Moor already changes with my poison:
Dangerous conceits° are in their natures poisons,
Which at the first are scarce found to distaste,°
But, with a little° act upon the blood,   325
Burn like the mines of sulfur. I did say so.

Enter OTHELLO.

Look, where he comes! Not poppy nor mandragora,°
Nor all the drowsy syrups of the world,
Shall ever medicine thee to that sweet sleep
Which thou owedst° yesterday.
Othello.   Ha! ha! False to me?   330
Iago.

Why, how now, general? No more of that.
Othello.

Avaunt! be gone! Thou hast set me on the rack.
I swear 'tis better to be much abused
Than but to know't a little.
Iago.   How now, my lord?

---

316. **Be not acknown on't:** Do not admit to any knowledge of it.
323. **conceits:** conceptions; ideas.
324. **distaste:** be distasteful.
325. **with a little:** in a short while.
327. **mandragora:** drug causing sleepiness, made from the root of the
     mandrake plant.
330. **owedst:** possessed.

Othello.

What sense had I of her stol'n hours of lust?   335
I saw't not, thought it not, it harmed not me;
I slept the next night well, fed well, was free° and
    merry;
I found not Cassio's kisses on her lips.
He that is robbed, not wanting° what is stol'n,
Let him not know't, and he's not robbed at all.   340

Iago.

I am sorry to hear this.

Othello.

I had been happy if the general camp,
Pioners° and all, had tasted her sweet body,
So° I had nothing known. O now, forever
Farewell the tranquil mind! Farewell content!   345
Farewell the plumed troop, and the big° wars
That make ambition virtue! O, farewell!
Farewell the neighing steed and the shrill trump,
The spirit-stirring drum, th' ear-piercing fife,
The royal banner, and all quality,°   350
Pride, pomp, and circumstance° of glorious war!
And O you mortal engines° whose rude throats
Th' immortal Jove's dread clamors° counterfeit,
Farewell! Othello's occupation's gone!

Iago.

Is't possible, my lord?   355

Othello.

Villain, be sure thou prove my love a whore!

---

337. **free:** untroubled; carefree.
339. **wanting:** missing.
343. **Pioners:** manual laborers (the lowest level of soldiers).
344. **So:** if only.
346. **big:** stately; glorious.
350. **quality:** essential nature.
351. **circumstance:** pageantry.
352. **mortal engines:** deadly cannon.
353. **Jove's dread clamors:** thunder. (In Roman mythology, Jove, or
     Jupiter, is the god of thunder and the skies.)

Be sure of it; give me the ocular proof;
Or, by the worth of mine eternal soul,
Thou hadst been better have been born a dog
Than answer my waked wrath!

Iago.   Is't come to this?   360

Othello.

Make me to see't; or at the least so prove it
That the probation° bear no hinge nor loop
To hang a doubt on—or woe upon thy life!

Iago.

My noble lord—

Othello.

If thou dost slander her and torture me,   365
Never pray more; abandon all remorse;
On horror's head horrors accumulate;
Do deeds to make heaven weep, all earth amazed;°
For nothing canst thou to damnation add
Greater than that.

Iago.   O grace! O heaven forgive me!   370

Are you a man? Have you a soul or sense?
God b' wi' you! Take mine office. O wretched fool,°
That lov'st to make thine honesty a vice!°
O monstrous world! Take note, take note, O world,
To be direct and honest is not safe.   375
I thank you for this profit,° and from hence
I'll love no friend, sith° love breeds such offense.

Othello.

Nay, stay. Thou shouldst be honest.

Iago.

I should be wise; for honesty's a fool
And loses that it works for.

---

362. **probation:** proof.
368. **amazed:** horrified.
372. **O wretched fool:** (Iago is addressing himself.)
373. **vice:** failing (because taken to excess).
376. **profit:** profitable lesson.
377. **sith:** since.

Othello.   By the world,   380
  I think my wife be honest, and think she is not;
  I think that thou art just and think thou art not.
  I'll have some proof. Her name, that was as fresh
  As Dian's° visage, is now begrimed and black
  As mine own face. If there be cords, or knives,   385
  Poison, or fire, or suffocating streams,
  I'll not endure it. Would I were satisfied!
Iago.
  I see, sir, you are eaten up with passion.
  I do repent me that I put it to you.
  You would be satisfied?
Othello.   Would? Nay, and I will.   390
Iago.
  And may; but how? How satisfied, my lord?
  Would you, the supervisor,° grossly gape on?
  Behold her topped?
Othello.   Death and damnation! O!
Iago.
  It were a tedious° difficulty, I think,
  To bring them to that prospect. Damn them then,   395
  If ever mortal eyes do see them bolster°
  More° than their own! What then? How then?
  What shall I say? Where's satisfaction?
  It is impossible you should see this,
  Were they as prime° as goats, as hot as monkeys,   400
  As salt° as wolves in pride,° and fools as gross
  As ignorance made drunk. But yet, I say,
  If imputation and strong circumstances
  Which lead directly to the door of truth
  Will give you satisfaction, you might have't.   405

---

384. **Dian's:** Diana's. (In Roman mythology, Diana is the goddess of chastity and the moon.)
392. **supervisor:** onlooker.
394. **tedious:** difficult to arrange.
396. **bolster:** go to bed.
397. **More:** other.
400. **prime:** lustful; lecherous.
401. **salt:** lustful. **pride:** heat.

Othello.

Give me a living reason she's disloyal.

Iago.

I do not like the office.°

But sith I am entered in this cause so far,

Pricked° to't by foolish honesty and love,

I will go on. I lay with Cassio lately,   410

And being troubled with a raging tooth,

I could not sleep.

There are a kind of men so loose of soul

That in their sleeps will mutter their affairs.

One of this kind is Cassio.   415

In sleep I heard him say, "Sweet Desdemona,

Let us be wary, let us hide our loves!"

And then, sir, would he gripe° and wring my hand,

Cry "O sweet creature!" Then kiss me hard,

As if he plucked up kisses by the roots   420

That grew upon my lips; laid his leg o'er my thigh,

And sigh, and kiss, and then cry, "Cursèd fate

That gave thee to the Moor!"

Othello.

O monstrous! monstrous!

Iago.   Nay, this was but his dream.

Othello.

But this denoted a foregone conclusion,°   425

'Tis a shrewd doubt,° though it be but a dream.

Iago.

And this may help to thicken° other proofs

That do demonstrate thinly.

Othello.   I'll tear her all to pieces!

Iago.

Nay, yet be wise. Yet we see nothing done;

---

407. **office:** duty.
409. **Pricked:** spurred.
418. **gripe:** seize.
425. **foregone conclusion:** actual occurrence.
426. **shrewd doubt:** very suspicious circumstance.
427. **thicken:** substantiate.

She may be honest yet. Tell me but this: 430
Have you not sometimes seen a handkerchief
Spotted with strawberries° in your wife's hand?

Othello.

I gave her such a one; 'twas my first gift.

Iago.

I know not that; but such a handkerchief—
I am sure it was your wife's—did I today   435
See Cassio wipe his beard with.

Othello.   If it be that—

Iago.

If it be that, or any that was hers,
It speaks against her with the other proofs.

Othello.

O, that the slave° had forty thousand lives!
One is too poor, too weak for my revenge.   440
Now do I see 'tis true. Look here, Iago:
All my fond° love thus do I blow to heaven.
'Tis gone.
Arise, black vengeance, from the hollow hell!
Yield up, O Love, thy crown and hearted throne°   445
To tyrannous hate! Swell, bosom, with thy fraught,°
For 'tis of aspics'° tongues.

Iago.   Yet be content.

Othello.

O, blood, blood, blood!

Iago.

Patience, I say. Your mind may change.

Othello.

Never, Iago. Like to the Pontic Sea,°   450
Whose icy current and compulsive course

---

432. **Spotted with strawberries:** embroidered with a strawberry pattern.
439. **slave:** Cassio.
442. **fond:** foolish.
445. **hearted throne:** throne located in the heart.
446. **fraught:** burden.
447. **aspics':** asps'; venomous serpents'.
450. **Pontic Sea:** Black Sea.

Nev'r keeps retiring ebb, but keeps due on
To the Propontic° and the Hellespont,°
Even so my bloody thoughts, with violent pace,
Shall nev'r look back, nev'r ebb to humble love,   455
Till that a capable° and wide revenge
Swallow them up. [*Kneeling.*] Now, by yond marble°
    heaven,
In the due reverence of a sacred vow
I here engage my words.

Iago.   Do not rise yet.

Kneels.

Witness, you ever-burning lights above,   460
You elements that clip° us round about,
Witness that here Iago doth give up
The execution° of his wit,° hands, heart,
To wronged Othello's service! Let him command,
And to obey shall be in me remorse,°   465
What bloody business ever.°

They rise.

Othello.   I greet thy love,
Not with vain thanks, but with acceptance bounteous,
And will upon the instant put thee to't.°
Within these three days let me hear thee say
That Cassio's not alive.   470

Iago.
My friend is dead. 'Tis done at your request.
But let her live.

---

453. **Propontic:** Sea of Marmara. **Hellespont:** Dardanelles strait (links the
    Sea of Marmara and the Aegean Sea).
456. **capable:** comprehensive; ample.
457. **marble:** (that is, shining like polished marble).
461. **clip:** encompass.
463. **execution:** exercise; action. **wit:** intelligence.
465. **remorse:** pity.
466. **ever:** soever.
468. **to't:** to the task.

Othello.   Damn her, lewd minx!° O, damn her!
    Damn her!
    Come, go with me apart. I will withdraw
    To furnish me with some swift means of death
    For the fair devil. Now art thou my lieutenant.   475
Iago.
    I am your own forever.

Exeunt.

Scene 4. *Before the castle.*

Enter DESDEMONA, EMILIA, *and* CLOWN.

Desdemona. Do you know, sirrah,° where Lieutenant
    Cassio lies?°
Clown. I dare not say he lies° anywhere.
Desdemona. Why, man?
Clown. He's a soldier, and for me to say a soldier lies,   5
    'tis stabbing.
Desdemona. Go to. Where lodges he?
Clown. To tell you where he lodges is to tell you where
    I lie.
Desdemona. Can anything be made of this?   10
Clown. I know not where he lodges, and for me to
    devise a lodging and say he lies here or he lies there
    were to lie in mine own throat.°
Desdemona. Can you enquire him out, and be edified
    by report?   15
Clown. I will catechize the world for him; that is, make
    questions, and by them answer.

---

472. **minx:** wanton.
III.4.1.   **sirrah:** (term of address to a social inferior).
  2. **lies:** lodges; lives.
  3. **lies:** tells an untruth.
 13. **lie . . . throat:** deliberately tell an absolute untruth.

Desdemona. Seek him, bid him come hither. Tell him I
　　have moved my lord on his behalf and hope all will
　　be well.　　　　　　　　　　　　　　　　　　　　　　20

Clown. To do this is within the compass° of man's wit,
　　and therefore I will attempt the doing it.　　　[*Exit.*]

Desdemona. Where should I lose the handkerchief,
　　Emilia?

Emilia. I know not, madam.　　　　　　　　　　　　25

Desdemona.
　　Believe me, I had rather have lost my purse
　　Full of crusadoes.° And but my noble Moor
　　Is true of mind and made of no such baseness
　　As jealous creatures are, it were enough
　　To put him to ill thinking.

Emilia.　　　　　　　　　Is he not jealous?　　　　30

Desdemona.
　　Who? He? I think the sun where he was born
　　Drew all such humors° from him.

Emilia.　　　　　　　　　　Look where he comes.

Enter OTHELLO.

Desdemona.
　　I will not leave him now till Cassio
　　Be called to him. How is't with you, my lord?

Othello.
　　Well, my good lady. [*Aside.*] O, hardness to
　　　　dissemble!—　　　　　　　　　　　　　　　　　35
　　How do you, Desdemona?

Desdemona.　　　　　　　Well, my good lord.

Othello.
　　Give me your hand. The hand is moist, my lady.

　21.　**compass:** range; reach.
　27.　**crusadoes:** Portuguese gold coins.
　32.　**humors:** traits. (Four bodily fluids, or humors, were thought to
　　　determine a person's temperament. The reference here is probably to
　　　bile, considered the cause of jealousy.)

Desdemona.

It yet hath felt no age nor known no sorrow.

Othello.

This argues fruitfulness and liberal heart,
Hot, hot, and moist.° This hand of yours requires   40
A sequester° from liberty, fasting, and prayer,
Much castigation,° exercise devout;°
For here's a young and sweating devil° here
That commonly rebels. 'Tis a good hand,
A frank one.

Desdemona.   You may, indeed, say so;   45
For 'twas that hand that gave away my heart.

Othello.

A liberal hand! The hearts of old gave hands,
But our new heraldry is hands, not hearts.°

Desdemona.

I cannot speak of this. Come now, your promise!

Othello.

What promise, chuck?°   50

Desdemona.

I have sent to bid Cassio come speak with you.

Othello.

I have a salt and sorry rheum° offends me.
Lend me thy handkerchief.

Desdemona.   Here, my lord.

Othello.

That which I gave you.

Desdemona.   I have it not about me.

Othello. Not?

---

40. **Hot, hot, and moist:** (A hot, moist hand was considered a sign of an amorous or lustful nature.)
41. **sequester:** separation.
42. **castigation:** corrective discipline. **exercise devout:** religious observance.
43. **sweating devil:** spirit of sexual desire.
48. **But . . . hearts:** but in our times the joining of hands no longer signifies the giving of hearts.
50. **chuck:** (term of endearment).
52. **salt and sorry rheum:** severe running head cold.

Desdemona.   No, indeed, my lord.

Othello.   That's a fault.   55

That handkerchief

Did an Egyptian to my mother give.

She was a charmer,° and could almost read

The thoughts of people. She told her, while she kept it

'Twould make her amiable° and subdue my father   60

Entirely to her love; but if she lost it

Or made a gift of it, my father's eye

Should hold her loathèd, and his spirits should hunt

After new fancies.° She, dying, gave it me,

And bid me, when my fate would have me wived,   65

To give it her. I did so; and take heed on't;

Make it a darling like your precious eye.

To lose't or give't away were such perdition°

As nothing else could match.

Desdemona.   Is't possible?

Othello.

'Tis true. There's magic in the web° of it.   70

A sibyl° that had numbered in the world

The sun to course two hundred compasses,°

In her prophetic fury° sewed the work;

The worms were hallowed that did breed the silk,

And it was dyed in mummy° which the skillful   75

Conserved of maidens' hearts.

Desdemona.   Indeed? Is't true?

---

58. **charmer:** sorcerer; enchanter.
60. **amiable:** desirable; lovable.
64. **fancies:** loves.
68. **perdition:** loss.
70. **web:** weaving.
71. **sibyl:** prophet.
72. **compasses:** yearly circlings. (The prophet was two hundred years old.)
73. **prophetic fury:** frenzy of inspiration.
75. **mummy:** purported magical or medicinal preparation supposedly drained from embalmed bodies.

Othello.

Most veritable. Therefore look to't well.

Desdemona.

Then would to God that I had never seen't!

Othello. Ha! Wherefore?

Desdemona.

Why do you speak so startingly° and rash?   80

Othello.

Is't lost? Is't gone? Speak, is it out o' th' way?°

Desdemona. Heaven bless us!

Othello. Say you?

Desdemona.

It is not lost. But what an if it were?

Othello. How?   85

Desdemona.

I say it is not lost.

Othello.   Fetch't, let me see't!

Desdemona.

Why, so I can, sir; but I will not now.

This is a trick to put me from my suit:

Pray you let Cassio be received again.

Othello.

Fetch me the handkerchief! My mind misgives.   90

Desdemona.

Come, come!

You'll never meet a more sufficient° man—

Othello.

The handkerchief!

Desdemona.   I pray, talk me of Cassio.

Othello.

The handkerchief!

Desdemona.   A man that all his time

Hath founded his good fortunes on your love,   95

Shared dangers with you—

---

80. **startingly:** disjointedly.
81. **out o' th' way:** lost; misplaced.
92. **sufficient:** able; complete.

Othello.

The handkerchief!

Desdemona.

I' faith, you are to blame.

Othello. Away!   [*Exit.*]

Emilia. Is not this man jealous?   100

Desdemona.

I nev'r saw this before.

Sure there's some wonder° in this handkerchief;

I am most unhappy in the loss of it.

Emilia.

'Tis not a year or two shows us a man.

They are all but stomachs, and we all but food;   105

To eat us hungerly, and when they are full,

They belch us.

Enter CASSIO *and* IAGO.

                              Look you, Cassio and my husband!

Iago.

There is no other way; 'tis she must do't.

And lo the happiness!° Go and importune her.

Desdemona.

How now, good Cassio? What's the news with you?   110

Cassio.

Madam, my former suit. I do beseech you

That by your virtuous° means I may again

Exist, and be a member of his love

Whom I with all the office° of my heart

Entirely honor. I would not be delayed.   115

If my offense be of such mortal° kind

That nor my service past, nor present sorrows,

Nor purposed merit in futurity,

---

102. **wonder:** magical quality.
109. **happiness:** good luck; fortunate occurrence.
112. **virtuous:** effective.
114. **office:** duty; loyal service.
116. **mortal:** fatal.

Can ransom me into his love again,
But° to know so must be my benefit.   120
So shall I clothe me in a forced content,
And shut myself up in some other course
To fortune's alms.°
Desdemona.   Alas, thrice-gentle Cassio,
My advocation° is not now in tune.
My lord is not my lord; nor should I know him   125
Were he in favor° as in humor° altered.
So help me every spirit sanctified
As I have spoken for you all my best
And stood within the blank° of his displeasure
For my free speech. You must awhile be patient.   130
What I can do I will; and more I will
Than for myself I dare. Let that suffice you.
Iago.
Is my lord angry?
Emilia.   He went hence but now,
And certainly in strange unquietness.
Iago.
Can he be angry? I have seen the cannon   135
When it hath blown his ranks into the air
And, like the devil, from his very arm
Puff'd his own brother. And is he angry?
Something of moment° then. I will go meet him.
There's matter in't indeed if he be angry.   140
Desdemona.
I prithee, do so.

Exit IAGO.

---

120. **But:** merely.
123. **fortune's alms:** mercy of fortune.
124. **advocation:** advocacy.
126. **favor:** appearance. **humor:** mood.
129. **within the blank:** at the bull's-eye.
139. **moment:** immediate importance.

Something sure of state,°
Either from Venice or some unhatched practice°
Made demonstrable here in Cyprus to him,
Hath puddled° his clear spirit; and in such cases
Men's natures wrangle with inferior things,   145
Though great ones are their object. 'Tis even so.
For let our finger ache, and it endues°
Our other, healthful members even to a sense
Of pain. Nay, we must think men are not gods,
Nor of them look for such observancy°   150
As fits the bridal. Beshrew me° much, Emilia,
I was, unhandsome° warrior as I am,
Arraigning his unkindness with my soul;
But now I find I had suborned the witness,°
And he's indicted falsely.

Emilia.   Pray heaven it be   155
State matters, as you think, and no conception
Nor no jealous toy° concerning you.

Desdemona.
Alas the day! I never gave him cause.

Emilia.
But jealous souls will not be answered so;
They are not ever jealous for the cause,   160
But jealous for they're jealous. It is a monster
Begot upon itself, born on itself.

Desdemona.
Heaven keep that monster from Othello's mind!

Emilia. Lady, amen.

---

141. **of state:** concerning affairs of state.
142. **unhatched practice:** undiscovered conspiracy.
144. **puddled:** muddied.
147. **endues:** leads.
150. **observancy:** attentiveness.
151. **Beshrew me:** (mild oath).
152. **unhandsome:** insufficient; unskillful.
154. **suborned the witness:** induced the witness to give false testimony.
157. **toy:** fancy; whim.

Desdemona.

> I will go seek him. Cassio, walk here about.　　　165
> If I do find him fit, I'll move your suit
> And seek to effect it to my uttermost.

Cassio.

> I humbly thank your ladyship.

> *Exeunt* DESDEMONA *and* EMILIA.

Enter BIANCA.

Bianca.

> Save° you, friend Cassio!

Cassio.　　　　　　　　　　What make you from home?

> How is't with you, my most fair Bianca?　　　170
> I' faith, sweet love, I was coming to your house.

Bianca.

> And I was going to your lodging, Cassio.
> What, keep a week away? Seven days and nights?
> Eight score eight hours? And lovers' absent hours
> More tedious than the dial° eightscore times?　　　175
> O weary reck'ning!°

Cassio.　　　　　　　　Pardon me, Bianca.

> I have this while with leaden thoughts been pressed,
> But I shall in a more continuate° time
> Strike off this score° of absence. Sweet Bianca,

Gives her DESDEMONA's *handkerchief.*

> Take me this work out.°

Bianca.　　　　　　　　O Cassio, whence came this?　　　180

> This is some token from a newer friend.°

---

169. **Save:** God save.
175. **dial:** complete revolution of the clock.
176. **reck'ning:** addition.
178. **continuate:** uninterrupted.
179. **Strike off this score:** pay this bill; settle this account.
180. **Take . . . out:** Copy this embroidered pattern for me.
181. **friend:** mistress.

To the felt absence now I feel a cause.
Is't come to this? Well, well.

Cassio.   Go to, woman!
Throw your vile guesses in the devil's teeth,
From whence you have them. You are jealous now   185
That this is from some mistress, some remembrance.
No, by my faith, Bianca.

Bianca.   Why, whose is it?

Cassio.
I know not neither. I found it in my chamber.
I like the work well; ere it be demanded,°
As like enough it will, I would have it copied.   190
Take it and do't, and leave me for this time.

Bianca.
Leave you! Wherefore?

Cassio.
I do attend here on the general
And think it no addition,° nor my wish,
To have him see me womaned.

Bianca.   Why, I pray you?   195

Cassio.
Not that I love you not.

Bianca.   But that you do not love me!
I pray you bring° me on the way a little,
And say if I shall see you soon at night.

Cassio.
'Tis but a little way that I can bring you,
For I attend here; but I'll see you soon.   200

Bianca.
'Tis very good. I must be circumstanced.°

                                Exeunt.

---

189. **demanded:** inquired after (by the one who lost it).
194. **addition:** credit to me.
197. **bring:** accompany.
201. **be circumstanced:** accept conditions as they are.

Act IV

Scene 1. *Cyprus. Before the castle.*

Enter OTHELLO *and* IAGO.

Iago.
  Will you think so?
Othello.   Think so, Iago?
Iago.   What,
  To kiss in private?
Othello.   An unauthorized kiss?
Iago.
  Or to be naked with her friend in bed
  An hour or more, not meaning any harm?
Othello.
  Naked in bed, Iago, and not mean harm?   5
  It is hypocrisy against the devil.
  They that mean virtuously, and yet do so,
  The devil their virtue tempts, and they tempt heaven.
Iago.
  So they do nothing, 'tis a venial° slip.
  But if I give my wife a handkerchief—   10
Othello. What then?
Iago.
  Why, then, 'tis hers, my lord; and being hers,
  She may, I think, bestow't on any man.
Othello.
  She is protectress of her honor too.
  May she give that?   15

IV.1.9.   **venial:** pardonable.

Iago.

> Her honor is an essence that's not seen;
> They have it very oft that have it not.
> But for the handkerchief—

Othello.

> By heaven, I would most gladly have forgot it!
> Thou said'st—O, it comes o'er my memory   20
> As doth the raven o'er the infected house,°
> Boding to all—he had my handkerchief.

Iago.

> Ay, what of that?

Othello.   That's not so good now.

Iago.

> What if I had said I had seen him do you wrong?
> Or heard him say—as knaves be such abroad   25
> Who having, by their own importunate suit,
> Or voluntary dotage° of some mistress,
> Convincèd or supplied° them, cannot choose
> But they must blab—

Othello.   Hath he said anything?

Iago.

> He hath, my lord; but be you well assured,   30
> No more than he'll unswear.

Othello.   What hath he said?

Iago.

> Why, that he did—I know not what he did.

Othello. What? What?

Iago. Lie—

Othello.

> With her?

Iago.   With her, on her; what you will.   35

---

21. **raven . . . house:** (It was believed that ravens hovered over houses in which someone suffered from disease, such as the plague.)
27. **voluntary dotage:** willing infatuation.
28. **Convincèd or supplied:** seduced or satisfied.

Othello. Lie with her? Lie on her?—We say lie on her
when they belie° her.—Lie with her! Zounds, that's
fulsome.°—Handkerchief—confessions—handkerchief!—To confess, and be hanged for his labor—
first to be hanged, and then to confess! I tremble at it.　40
Nature would not invest herself in such shadowing
passion without some instruction.° It is not words
that shakes me thus.—Pish! Noses, ears, and lips?
Is't possible?—Confess—Handkerchief?—O devil!

Falls in a trance.

Iago.

　Work on,　　　　　　　　　　　　　　　　　　　　45
　My med'cine work! Thus credulous fools are caught,
　And many worthy and chaste dames even thus,
　All guiltless, meet reproach.° What, ho! My lord!
　My lord, I say! Othello!

Enter CASSIO.

　　　　　　　　　　　　How now, Cassio!

Cassio.

　What's the matter?　　　　　　　　　　　　　　　　50

Iago.

　My lord is fall'n into an epilepsy.
　This is his second fit; he had one yesterday.

Cassio.

　Rub him about the temples.

Iago.　　　　　　　　　　　　No, forbear;
　The lethargy° must have his quiet course.
　If not, he foams at mouth and by and by　　　　　55
　Breaks out to savage madness. Look, he stirs.

---

　37. belie: vilify.
　38. fulsome: foul.
41–42. **Nature . . . instruction:** (In other words, I would not feel such
　　strong emotion were there not a basis in fact for my emotion.)
　48. reproach: shame.
　54. lethargy: coma.

Do you withdraw yourself a little while.
He will recover straight. When he is gone,
I would on great occasion° speak with you.

Exit CASSIO.

How is it, general? Have you not hurt your head?   60
Othello.

Dost thou mock me?°
Iago.   I mock you not, by heaven.
Would you would bear your fortune like a man.
Othello.

A hornèd man's a monster and a beast.
Iago.

There's many a beast then in a populous city,
And many a civil° monster.   65
Othello.

Did he confess it?
Iago.   Good sir, be a man.
Think every bearded fellow that's but yoked°
May draw° with you. There's millions now alive
That nightly lie in those unproper° beds
Which they dare swear peculiar.° Your case is better.   70
O, 'tis the spite of hell, the fiend's arch-mock,
To lip° a wanton in a secure couch,°
And to suppose her chaste! No, let me know;
And knowing what I am,° I know what she shall be.
Othello.

O, thou art wise! 'Tis certain.

___

59. **great occasion:** a very important matter.
61. **Dost thou mock me?** (Othello rightly takes Iago's question about his head as a reference to the cuckold's horns.)
65. **civil:** living in a city; (possibly) civilized.
67. **yoked:** married, or burdened (by being wronged).
68. **draw:** pull (like yoked, and horned, oxen).
69. **unproper:** not solely their own.
70. **peculiar:** solely their own.
72. **lip:** kiss. **secure couch:** bed free from suspicion.
74. **knowing what I am:** knowing that I am a cuckold.

Iago.   Stand you awhile apart;   75
   Confine yourself but in a patient list.°
   Whilst you were here, o'erwhelmèd with your grief—
   A passion most unsuiting such a man—
   Cassio came hither. I shifted him away°
   And laid good 'scuses upon your ecstasy;°   80
   Bade him anon return, and here speak with me;
   The which he promised. Do but encave° yourself,
   And mark the fleers,° the gibes, and notable° scorns
   That dwell in every region of his face.
   For I will make him tell the tale anew: 85
   Where, how, how oft, how long ago, and when
   He hath, and is again to cope° your wife.
   I say, but mark his gesture. Marry patience,
   Or I shall say you're all in all in spleen,°
   And nothing of a man.

Othello.   Dost thou hear, Iago?   90
   I will be found most cunning in my patience;
   But—dost thou hear?—most bloody.

Iago.   That's not amiss;
   But yet keep time° in all. Will you withdraw?

OTHELLO *retires.*

   Now will I question Cassio of Bianca,
   A huswife° that by selling her desires   95
   Buys herself bread and cloth. It is a creature
   That dotes on Cassio, as 'tis the strumpet's plague
   To beguile many and be beguiled by one.
   He, when he hears of her, cannot refrain
   From the excess of laughter. Here he comes.   100

---

76. **in a patient list:** within the bounds of self-control.
79. **shifted him away:** got rid of him by a strategem.
80. **ecstasy:** trance.
82. **encave:** conceal.
83. **fleers:** sneers. **notable:** obvious.
87. **cope:** meet; have sex with.
89. **all . . . spleen:** utterly governed by passion or anger.
93. **keep time:** be controlled (reference to a term from music).
95. **huswife:** (here) hussy.

Enter CASSIO.

As he shall smile, Othello shall go mad;
And his unbookish° jealousy must construe
Poor Cassio's smiles, gestures, and light behaviors
Quite in the wrong. How do you, lieutenant?

Cassio.

The worser that you give me the addition°   105
Whose want even kills me.

Iago.

Ply Desdemona well, and you are sure on't.

Speaks lower.

Now, if this suit lay in Bianca's power,
How quickly should you speed!

Cassio.   Alas, poor caitiff!°

Othello.

Look how he laughs already!   110

Iago.

I never knew woman love man so.

Cassio.

Alas, poor rogue! I think, i' faith, she loves me.

Othello.

Now he denies it faintly, and laughs it out.

Iago.

Do you hear, Cassio?

Othello.   Now he importunes him
To tell it o'er. Go to! Well said, well said!   115

Iago.

She gives it out that you shall marry her.
Do you intend it?

Cassio. Ha, ha, ha!

Othello.

Do ye triumph, Roman? Do you triumph?

---

102. **unbookish:** uninstructed; ignorant.
105. **addition:** title.
109. **caitiff:** wretch.

Cassio. I marry her? What, a customer?° Prithee bear   120
some charity to my wit;° do not think it so unwhole-
some. Ha, ha, ha!

Othello. So, so, so, so. They laugh that win.

Iago. Faith, the cry° goes that you shall marry her.

Cassio. Prithee, say true.   125

Iago. I am a very villain else.

Othello. Have you scored° me? Well.

Cassio. This is the monkey's own giving out. She is
persuaded I will marry her out of her own love and
flattery,° not out of my promise.   130

Othello. Iago beckons me; now he begins the story.

Cassio. She was here even now; she haunts me in
every place. I was the other day talking on the sea
bank with certain Venetians, and thither comes the
bauble, and falls me thus about my neck—   135

Othello. Crying "O dear Cassio!" as it were. His gesture
imports it.

Cassio. So hangs, and lolls, and weeps upon me; so
shakes and pulls me! Ha, ha, ha!

Othello. Now he tells how she plucked him to my   140
chamber. O, I see that nose of yours, but not that
dog I shall throw it to.

Cassio. Well, I must leave her company.

Iago. Before me!° Look where she comes.

Enter BIANCA.

Cassio. 'Tis such another fitchew!° Marry a perfumed   145
one. What do you mean by this haunting of me?

---

120. **customer:** (here) prostitute.
121. **wit:** judgment.
124. **cry:** rumor.
127. **scored:** branded; wounded. (The term may also mean "made my
reckoning.")
130. **flattery:** self-flattery.
144. **Before me:** Upon my soul! (an exclamation of surprise).
145. **fitchew:** polecat (noted for its strong smell).

Bianca. Let the devil and his dam° haunt you! What
  did you mean by that same handkerchief you gave
  me even now? I was a fine fool to take it. I must take
  out the work? A likely piece of work° that you   150
  should find it in your chamber and know not who
  left it there! This is some minx's token, and I must
  take out the work? There! Give it your hobbyhorse.°
  Wheresoever you had it, I'll take out no work on't.
Cassio. How now, my sweet Bianca? How now? how   155
  now?
Othello. By heaven, that should be my handkerchief!
Bianca. An you'll come to supper tonight, you may; an
  you will not, come when you are next prepared for.°

                                          Exit.
Iago. After her, after her!   160
Cassio. Faith, I must; she'll rail in the streets else.
Iago. Will you sup there?
Cassio. Yes, I intend so.
Iago. Well, I may chance to see you, for I would very
  fain speak with you.   165
Cassio. Prithee come. Will you?
Iago. Go to, say no more.

                                 Exit CASSIO.

Othello. [*Advancing.*] How shall I murder him, Iago?
Iago. Did you perceive how he laughed at his vice?
Othello. O Iago!   170
Iago. And did you see the handkerchief?
Othello. Was that mine?
Iago. Yours by this hand! And to see how he prizes the
  foolish woman your wife! She gave it him, and he
  hath giv'n it his whore.   175

---

147. **dam:** mother.
150. **piece of work:** story.
153. **hobbyhorse:** loose woman; prostitute.
159. **prepared for:** expected (that is, never).

Othello. I would have him nine years a-killing!—A fine
woman, a fair woman, a sweet woman?

Iago. Nay, you must forget that.

Othello. Ay, let her rot, and perish, and be damned
tonight; for she shall not live. No, my heart is turned   180
to stone; I strike it, and it hurts my hand. O, the
world hath not a sweeter creature! She might lie by
an emperor's side and command him tasks.

Iago. Nay, that's not your way.°

Othello. Hang her! I do but say what she is. So delicate   185
with her needle. An admirable musician. O, she will
sing the savageness out of a bear! Of so high and
plenteous wit and invention°—

Iago. She's the worse for all this.

Othello. O, a thousand, a thousand times. And then, of   190
so gentle a condition?°

Iago. Ay, too gentle.°

Othello. Nay, that's certain. But yet the pity of it, Iago.
O Iago, the pity of it, Iago.

Iago. If you are so fond over° her iniquity, give her patent   195
to offend; for if it touch not you, it comes near nobody.

Othello. I will chop her into messes!° Cuckold me!

Iago. O, 'tis foul in her.

Othello. With mine officer!

Iago. That's fouler.   200

Othello. Get me some poison, Iago, this night. I'll not
expostulate° with her, lest her body and beauty
unprovide my mind° again. This night, Iago.

---

184. **way:** proper course (of thought).
188. **invention:** imagination.
191. **gentle a condition:** well-born.
192. **gentle:** kind and yielding (to men).
195. **fond over:** foolish over; doting on.
197. **messes:** pieces of meat; bits.
202. **expostulate:** argue at length.
203. **unprovide my mind:** weaken my resolve.

Iago. Do it not with poison. Strangle her in her bed,
    even the bed she hath contaminated.   205
Othello. Good, good! The justice of it pleases. Very good!
Iago. And for Cassio, let me be his undertaker.° You shall
    hear more by midnight.
Othello. Excellent good!

A trumpet within.

    What trumpet is that same?   210
Iago. I warrant something from Venice.

Enter LODOVICO, DESDEMONA, *and* ATTENDANTS.

                              'Tis Lodovico.
    This comes from the duke. See, your wife's with him.
Lodovico.
    God save you, worthy general.
Othello.   With all my heart, sir.
Lodovico.
    The duke and senators of Venice greet you.

Gives him a letter.

Othello.
    I kiss the instrument of their pleasures.   215

Opens the letter and reads.

Desdemona.
    And what's the news, good cousin Lodovico?
Iago.
    I am very glad to see you, signior.
    Welcome to Cyprus.
Lodovico.
    I thank you. How does Lieutenant Cassio?
Iago.   Lives, sir.

---

207. **be his undertaker:** deal with him.

Desdemona.

    Cousin, there's fall'n between him and my lord   220

    An unkind° breach: but you shall make all well.

Othello. Are you sure of that?

Desdemona. My lord?

Othello. [*Reading.*] "This fail you not to do, as you will—"

Lodovico.

    He did not call; he's busy in the paper.   225

    Is there division 'twixt my lord and Cassio?

Desdemona.

    A most unhappy one. I would do much

    T' atone° them, for the love I bear to Cassio.

Othello.

    Fire and brimstone!

Desdemona.   My lord?

Othello.   Are you wise?

Desdemona.

    What, is he angry?

Lodovico.   May be th' letter moved him;   230

    For, as I think, they do command him home,

    Deputing Cassio in his government.°

Desdemona.

    Trust me, I am glad on't.°

Othello.   Indeed?

Desdemona.   My lord?

Othello.

    I am glad to see you mad.°

Desdemona.   Why, sweet Othello—

Othello. [*Striking her.*] Devil!   235

---

221. **unkind:** unnatural.
228. **atone:** reconcile.
232. **government:** office.
233. **on't:** of it.
234. **I . . . mad:** (The meaning is not clear. Perhaps Othello is remarking
     bitterly that he is glad to see Desdemona act insanely in openly
     professing her love and concern for Cassio.)

Desdemona.

I have not deserved this.

Lodovico.

My lord, this would not be believed in Venice,

Though I should swear I saw't. 'Tis very much.°

Make her amends; she weeps.

Othello.   O devil, devil!

If that the earth could teem with° woman's tears,   240

Each drop she falls° would prove a crocodile.°

Out of my sight!

Desdemona. [*Going.*] I will not stay to offend you.

Lodovico.

Truly, an obedient lady.

I do beseech your lordship, call her back.

Othello.

Mistress!

Desdemona. My lord?

Othello.   What would you with her, sir?   245

Lodovico.

Who? I, my lord?

Othello.

Ay! You did wish that I would make her turn.

Sir, she can turn, and turn, and yet go on

And turn again; and she can weep, sir, weep;

And she's obedient; as you say, obedient.   250

Very obedient. Proceed you in your tears.

Concerning this, sir—O well-painted passion!°

I am commanded home.—Get you away;

I'll send for you anon.—Sir, I obey the mandate

And will return to Venice.—Hence, avaunt!   255

Exit DESDEMONA.

---

238. **very much:** outrageous.

240. **teem with:** be impregnated by.

241. **falls:** lets fall. **prove a crocodile:** either turn into a crocodile or be the
same as (hypocritical) crocodile tears.

252. **well-painted passion:** cleverly simulated emotion.

Cassio shall have my place. And, sir, tonight
I do entreat that we may sup together.
You are welcome, sir, to Cyprus.—Goats and monkeys!°

Exit.

Lodovico.

Is this the noble Moor whom our full Senate
Call all in all sufficient? Is this the nature   260
Whom passion could not shake? Whose solid virtue
The shot of accident nor dart of chance
Could neither graze nor pierce?

Iago.   He is much changed.

Lodovico.

Are his wits safe? Is he not light of brain?

Iago.

He's that he is; I may not breathe my censure.   265
What he might be (if, what he might, he is not)
I would to heaven he were!°

Lodovico.   What, strike his wife?

Iago.

Faith, that was not so well; yet would I knew
That stroke would prove the worst.

Lodovico.   Is it his use?°
Or did the letters work upon his blood°   270
And new-create this fault?

Iago.   Alas, alas!
It is not honesty in me to speak
What I have seen and known. You shall observe him,
And his own courses will denote him so
That I may save my speech. Do but go after   275
And mark how he continues.

Lodovico.

I am sorry that I am deceived in him.

Exeunt.

---

258. **Goats and monkeys:** (animals considered lustful; see also III.3.400).

266–267. **if . . . were:** if he is not out of his mind, I wish to heaven he were (for that would excuse his wild behavior).

269. **use:** custom.

270. **blood:** passions.

Scene 2. *A room in the castle.*

Enter OTHELLO *and* EMILIA.

Othello.
    You have seen nothing then?
Emilia.
    Nor ever heard, nor ever did suspect.
Othello.
    Yes, you have seen Cassio and she together.
Emilia.
    But then I saw no harm, and then I heard
    Each syllable that breath made up between them.   5
Othello.
    What, did they never whisper?
Emilia.   Never, my lord.
Othello.
    Nor send you out o' th' way?
Emilia. Never.
Othello.
    To fetch her fan, her gloves, her mask, nor nothing?
Emilia. Never, my lord.   10
Othello. That's strange.
Emilia.
    I durst, my lord, to wager she is honest,
    Lay down my soul at stake.° If you think other,
    Remove your thought. It doth abuse your bosom.
    If any wretch have put this in your head,   15
    Let heaven requite it with the serpent's curse,°
    For if she be not honest, chaste, and true,
    There's no man happy. The purest of their wives
    Is foul as slander.
Othello.   Bid her come hither. Go.

                                        Exit EMILIA.

IV.2.13.   **at stake:** as the bet or wager.
  16.   the serpent's curse: God's curse on the serpent that tempted Adam
      and Eve in Eden (Genesis 3:14).

She says enough; yet she's a simple bawd   20
That cannot say as much.° This° is a subtle whore,
A closet lock and key° of villanous secrets,
And yet she'll kneel and pray; I have seen her do't.

Enter DESDEMONA *with* EMILIA.

Desdemona.
My lord, what is your will?
Othello.   Pray you, chuck, come hither.
Desdemona.
What is your pleasure?
Othello.   Let me see your eyes.   25
Look in my face.
Desdemona.   What horrible fancy's this?
Othello. [*To* EMILIA.]
Some of your function,° mistress:
Leave procreants° alone and shut the door;
Cough or cry "hem," if anybody come.
Your mystery, your mystery!° Nay, dispatch!   30

                              Exit EMILIA.

Desdemona.
Upon my knee, what doth your speech import?
I understand a fury in your words.
Othello.
Why, what art thou?
Desdemona.   Your wife, my lord; your true
And loyal wife.
Othello.   Come, swear it, damn thyself;
Lest, being like one of heaven, the devils themselves   35

20–21. she's . . . much: (A procuress, or brothel keeper, would have to be
    stupid not to be able to vouch for her mistress in the way Emilia has
    for Desdemona.)
  21. This: Desdemona.
  22. closet . . . key: a concealer.
  27. Some . . . function: do your job (as brothel keeper, and guard the
    door).
  28. procreants: lovers.
  30. mystery: trade; duties (of a procuress).

Should fear to seize thee. Therefore be double-
    damned:
Swear thou art honest.

Desdemona.   Heaven doth truly know it.

Othello.

Heaven truly knows that thou art false as hell.

Desdemona.

To whom, my lord? With whom? How am I false?

Othello.

O Desdemona! Away! Away! Away!   40

Desdemona.

Alas the heavy day! Why do you weep?
Am I the motive° of these tears, my lord?
If haply you my father do suspect
An instrument of this your calling back,
Lay not your blame on me. If you have lost him,   45
Why, I have lost him too.

Othello.   Had it pleased heaven
To try me with affliction, had they rained
All kinds of sores and shames on my bare head,
Steeped me in poverty to the very lips,
Given to captivity me and my utmost hopes,   50
I should have found in some place of my soul
A drop of patience. But, alas, to make me
The fixèd figure for the time of scorn
To point his slow and moving finger at.°
Yet could I bear that too, well, very well.   55
But there where I have garnered up° my heart,
Where either I must live or bear no life,
The fountain from the which my current runs
Or else dries up—to be discarded thence,
Or keep it as a cistern for foul toads   60
To knot and gender° in—turn thy complexion there,

---

42. **motive:** source; cause.
53–54. **fixèd . . . at:** eternal object of pity and mockery, pointed at like the
    numbers on a clock are by the slow-moving hour hand.
56. **garnered up:** stored; invested.
61. **knot and gender:** copulate and procreate.

Patience, thou young and rose-lipped cherubin!
I here look grim as hell!

Desdemona.

I hope my noble lord esteems me honest.°

Othello.

O, ay, as summer flies are in the shambles,°   65
That quicken even with blowing.° O thou weed,
Who art so lovely fair and smell'st so sweet
That the sense aches at thee, would thou hadst
    never been born!

Desdemona.

Alas, what ignorant sin have I committed?

Othello.

Was this fair paper, this most goodly book,   70
Made to write "whore" upon? What committed?
Committed? O thou public commoner,°
I should make very forges of my cheeks
That would to cinders burn up modesty,
Did I but speak thy deeds. What committed?   75
Heaven stops the nose at it, and the moon winks;°
The bawdy wind that kisses all it meets
Is hushed within the hollow mine° of earth
And will not hear't. What committed?
Impudent strumpet!

Desdemona.   By heaven, you do me wrong!   80

Othello.

Are you not a strumpet?

Desdemona.   No, as I am a Christian!
If to preserve this vessel° for my lord

---

64. **honest:** faithful; chaste.
65. **shambles:** slaughterhouse.
66. **quicken ... blowing:** come to life very quickly.
72. **commoner:** prostitute.
76. **winks:** shuts its eyes. (The moon symbolized chastity.)
78. **mine:** cave.
82. **vessel:** body.

From any other foul unlawful touch
Be not to be a strumpet, I am none.
Othello.
What, not a whore?
Desdemona.   No, as I shall be saved!   85
Othello.
Is't possible?
Desdemona.
O, heaven forgive us!
Othello.   I cry you mercy then.
I took you for that cunning whore of Venice
That married with Othello. [*Raising his voice.*] You,
    mistress,

Enter EMILIA.

That have the office opposite to Saint Peter,   90
And keep the gate of hell! You, you, ay, you!
We have done our course;° there's money for your
    pains.

Throws her some coins.

I pray you, turn the key and keep our counsel.   [*Exit.*]
Emilia.
Alas, what does this gentleman conceive?
How do you, madam? How do you, my good lady?   95
Desdemona. Faith, half asleep.°
Emilia.
Good madam, what's the matter with my lord?
Desdemona. With who?
Emilia. Why, with my lord, madam.
Desdemona.
Who is thy lord?
Emilia.   He that is yours, sweet lady.   100

---

92. **course:** business (of the brothel).
96. **half asleep:** dazed; stunned.

Desdemona.

    I have none. Do not talk to me, Emilia.

    I cannot weep, nor answers have I none

    But what should go by water.° Prithee tonight

    Lay on my bed my wedding sheets, remember;

    And call thy husband hither.

Emilia.   Here's a change indeed!   105

                                  Exit.

Desdemona.

    'Tis meet I should be used so, very meet.

    How have I been behaved, that he might stick

    The small'st opinion on my least misuse?°

Enter EMILIA *with* IAGO.

Iago.

    What is your pleasure, madam? How is't with you?

Desdemona.

    I cannot tell. Those that do teach young babes   110

    Do it with gentle means and easy tasks.

    He might have chid° me so; for, in good faith,

    I am a child to chiding.

Iago.   What is the matter, lady?

Emilia.

    Alas, Iago, my lord hath so bewhored her.

    Thrown such despite and heavy terms upon her   115

    As true hearts cannot bear.

Desdemona.

    Am I that name, Iago?

Iago.   What name, fair lady?

Desdemona.

    Such as she said my lord did say I was.

---

103. **go by water:** be expressed by tears.

107–108. **stick . . . misuse:** attach the least censure to my slightest
    misbehavior.

112. **chid:** (variant of *chided*) scolded; reproached.

Emilia.

    He called her whore. A beggar in his drink

    Could not have laid such terms upon his callet.°   120

Iago.

    Why did he so?

Desdemona.

    I do not know; I am sure I am none such.

Iago.

    Do not weep, do not weep. Alas the day.

Emilia.

    Hath she forsook so many noble matches,

    Her father and her country and her friends,   125

    To be called whore? Would it not make one weep?

Desdemona.

    It is my wretched fortune.

Iago.   Beshrew° him for't!

    How comes this trick° upon him?

Desdemona.   Nay, heaven doth know.

Emilia.

    I will be hanged if some eternal villain,

    Some busy and insinuating rogue,   130

    Some cogging,° cozening slave, to get some office,

    Have not devised this slander. I will be hanged else.

Iago.

    Fie, there is no such man! It is impossible.

Desdemona.

    If any such there be, heaven pardon him.

Emilia.

    A halter° pardon him! And hell gnaw his bones!   135

    Why should he call her whore? Who keeps her

        company?

---

120. **callet:** slut.
127. **Beshrew:** curse.
128. **trick:** delusion.
131. **cogging:** cheating; conniving.
135. **halter:** noose.

What place? What time? What form? What
    likelihood?
The Moor's abused by some most villainous knave,
Some base notorious knave, some scurvy fellow.
O heavens, that such companions thou'dst unfold,°   140
And put in every honest hand a whip
To lash the rascals naked through the world
Even from the east to th' west!

Iago.   Speak within door.°

Emilia.

O, fie upon them! Some such squire he was
That turned your wit the seamy side without°   145
And made you to suspect me with the Moor.

Iago.

You are a fool. Go to.

Desdemona.   Alas, Iago,
What shall I do to win my lord again?
Good friend, go to him, for, by this light of heaven,
I know not how I lost him. Here I kneel: 150
If e'er my will did trespass 'gainst his love,
Either in discourse of thought° or actual deed,
Or that° mine eyes, mine ears, or any sense
Delighted them in any other form;
Or that° I do not yet, and ever did,   155
And ever will (though he do shake me off
To beggarly divorcement) love him dearly,
Comfort forswear me. Unkindness may do much,
And his unkindness may defeat° my life,
But never taint my love. I cannot say "whore."   160
It does abhor me now I speak the word;

---

140. **unfold:** expose.
143. **within door:** with more control; less loudly.
145. **the seamy side without:** inside out.
152. **discourse of thought:** process of thinking.
153; 155. **that:** if.
159. **defeat:** ruin.

To do the act that might the addition earn
Not the world's mass of vanity could make me.
Iago.
I pray you be content. 'Tis but his humor.°
The business of the state does him offense.   165
Desdemona.
If 'twere no other.
Iago.   It is but so, I warrant.

Trumpets within.

Hark how these instruments summon to supper.
The messengers of Venice stay the meat.°
Go in, and weep not. All things shall be well.

Exeunt DESDEMONA *and* EMILIA.

Enter RODERIGO.

How now, Roderigo!   170
Roderigo. I do not find that thou deal'st justly with me.
Iago. What in the contrary?
Roderigo. Every day thou daff'st° me with some device,
    Iago, and rather, as it seems to me now, keep'st from
    me all conveniency° than suppliest me with the least   175
    advantage° of hope. I will indeed no longer endure
    it; nor am I yet persuaded to put up° in peace what
    already I have foolishly suffered.
Iago. Will you hear me, Roderigo?
Roderigo. I have heard too much, and your words and   180
    performances are no kin together.
Iago. You charge me most unjustly.

---

164. **humor:** mood.
168. **stay the meat:** are waiting for the meal.
173. **daff'st:** put off.
175. **conveniency:** that is needed.
176. **advantage:** furtherance; increase.
177. **put up:** tolerate; endure.

Roderigo. With naught but truth. I have wasted myself
out of my means. The jewels you have had from me
to deliver Desdemona would half have corrupted a   185
votarist.° You have told me she hath received them
and returned me expectations and comforts of sudden
respect° and acquaintance, but I find none.

Iago. Well, go to; very well.

Roderigo. Very well? Go to? I cannot go to, man; nor   190
'tis not very well. Nay, I think it is scurvy, and begin
to find myself fopped° in it.

Iago. Very well.

Roderigo. I tell you 'tis not very well. I will make
myself known to Desdemona. If she will return me   195
my jewels, I will give over my suit and repent my
unlawful solicitation. If not, assure yourself I will
seek satisfaction of you.

Iago. You have said now?

Roderigo. Ay, and said nothing but what I protest   200
intendment° of doing.

Iago. Why, now I see there's mettle° in thee, and even
from this instant do build on thee a better opinion
than ever before. Give me thy hand, Roderigo. Thou
hast taken against me a most just exception;° but yet   205
I protest I have dealt most directly in thy affair.

Roderigo. It hath not appeared.

Iago. I grant indeed it hath not appeared, and your suspicion is not without wit and judgment. But, Roderigo,
if thou hast that in thee indeed which I have greater   210
reason to believe now than ever—I mean purpose,
courage, and valor—this night show it. If thou the
next night following enjoy not Desdemona, take me

---

186. **votarist:** nun.
187–188.   **sudden respect:** immediate consideration.
192.   **fopped:** duped; misled.
200–201.   **protest intendment:** proclaim my intention.
202.   **mettle:** gumption; spirit.
205.   **exception:** complaint; objection.

from this world with treachery and devise engines
for° my life.   215

Roderigo. Well, what is it? Is it within reason and
compass?°

Iago. Sir, there is especial commission come from Venice
to depute Cassio in Othello's place.

Roderigo. Is that true? Why, then Othello and Desdemona   220
return again to Venice.

Iago. O, no; he goes into Mauritania° and taketh away
with him the fair Desdemona, unless his abode be
lingered here by some accident: wherein none can
be so determinate° as the removing of Cassio.   225

Roderigo. How do you mean, removing of him?

Iago. Why, by making him uncapable of Othello's
place—knocking out his brains.

Roderigo. And that you would have me to do?

Iago. Ay, if you dare do yourself a profit and a right. He   230
sups tonight with a harlotry, and thither will I go to
him. He knows not yet of his honorable fortune. If
you will watch his going thence, which I will fashion
to fall out° between twelve and one, you may take
him at your pleasure. I will be near to second your   235
attempt, and he shall fall between us. Come, stand
not amazed at it, but go along with me. I will show
you such a necessity in his death that you shall think
yourself bound to put it on him. It is now high
suppertime, and the night grows to waste. About it.   240

Roderigo. I will hear further reason for this.

Iago. And you shall be satisfied.

Exeunt.

214–215. engines for: plots against.
217. compass: realm of possibility.
222. Mauritania: a country in North Africa that once included the area of
modern Morocco and part of Algeria.
225. determinate: effective; conclusive.
234. fall out: have happen.

Scene 3. *Another room in the castle.*

Enter OTHELLO, LODOVICO, DESDEMONA, EMILIA, *and*
ATTENDANTS.

Lodovico.
I do beseech you, sir, trouble yourself no further.
Othello.
O, pardon me: 'twill do me good to walk.
Lodovico.
Madam, good night. I humbly thank your ladyship.
Desdemona.
Your honor is most welcome.
Othello.
Will you walk, sir? O, Desdemona.   5
Desdemona. My lord?
Othello. Get you to bed on th' instant; I will be returned
forthwith. Dismiss your attendant there. Look't be
done.
Desdemona. I will, my lord.   10

Exeunt OTHELLO, LODOVICO, *and* ATTENDANTS.

Emilia. How goes it now? He looks gentler than he did.
Desdemona.
He says he will return incontinent;°
He hath commanded me to go to bed,
And bade me to dismiss you.
Emilia.   Dismiss me?
Desdemona.
It was his bidding; therefore, good Emilia,   15
Give me my nightly wearing, and adieu.
We must not now displease him.
Emilia. I would you had never seen him!
Desdemona.
So would not I. My love doth so approve him

IV.3.12. **incontinent:** immediately.

That even his stubbornness, his checks,° his frowns— 20
Prithee unpin me—have grace and favor.

Emilia. I have laid these sheets you bade me on the bed.

Desdemona.
All's one.° Good Father, how foolish are our minds!
If I do die before, prithee shroud me
In one of these same sheets.

Emilia.   Come, come! You talk.° 25

Desdemona.
My mother had a maid called Barbary.
She was in love; and he she loved proved mad°
And did forsake her. She had a song of "Willow";
An old thing 'twas, but it expressed her fortune,
And she died singing it. That song tonight 30
Will not go from my mind; I have much to do
But to go hang my head all at one side
And sing it like poor Barbary. Prithee dispatch.

Emilia.
Shall I go fetch your nightgown?

Desdemona.
No, unpin me here. 35
This Lodovico is a proper man.

Emilia. A very handsome man.

Desdemona. He speaks well.

Emilia. I know a lady in Venice would have walked
barefoot to Palestine for a touch of his nether lip. 40

Desdemona. [*Singing.*]
"The poor soul sat sighing by a sycamore tree,
    Sing all a green willow;
Her hand on her bosom, her head on her knee,
    Sing willow, willow, willow.
The fresh streams ran by her, and murmured her moans; 45
    Sing willow, willow, willow;

---

20. **checks:** rebukes.
23. **All's one:** It doesn't matter.
25. **talk:** go on foolishly.
27. **proved mad:** turned out to be untrue.

Her salt tears fell from her, and soft'ned the stones—
 Sing willow, willow, willow—"
Lay by these.

Gives EMILIA *her clothes and resumes singing.*

 "Willow, willow—"
Prithee hie° thee; he'll come anon.   50

Sings.

 "Sing all a green willow must be my garland.
 Let nobody blame him; his scorn I approve"—
 Nay, that's not next. Hark! who is't that knocks?
Emilia. It is the wind.
Desdemona. [*Singing.*]
 "I called my love false love; but what said he then?   55
  Sing willow, willow, willow:
 If I court moe° women, you'll couch with moe men."
 So, get thee gone; good night. Mine eyes do itch.
 Doth that bode weeping?
Emilia.   'Tis neither here nor there.
Desdemona.
 I have heard it said so. O, these men, these men.   60
 Dost thou in conscience think, tell me, Emilia,
 That there be women do abuse° their husbands
 In such gross kind?
Emilia.   There be some such, no question.
Desdemona.
 Wouldst thou do such a deed for all the world?
Emilia.
 Why, would not you?
Desdemona.   No, by this heavenly light!°   65

---

50. **hie:** hurry.
57. **moe:** more.
62. **abuse:** deceive.
65. **heavenly light:** moonlight.

Emilia.

Nor I neither by this heavenly light.

I might do't as well i' th' dark.

Desdemona.

Wouldst thou do such a deed for all the world?

Emilia.

The world's a huge thing; it is a great price

For a small vice.

Desdemona.　　　In troth,° I think thou wouldst not.　　70

Emilia. In troth, I think I should; and undo't when I had

done. Marry, I would not do such a thing for a joint-

ring,° nor for measures of lawn,° nor for gowns,

petticoats, nor caps, nor any petty exhibition,° but

for the whole world? Why, who would not make her　　75

husband a cuckold to make him a monarch? I should

venture purgatory for't.

Desdemona. Beshrew me if I would do such a wrong

for the whole world.

Emilia. Why, the wrong is but a wrong i' th' world; and　　80

having the world for your labor, 'tis a wrong in your

own world, and you might quickly make it right.

Desdemona. I do not think there is any such woman.

Emilia. Yes, a dozen; and as many to th' vantage as

would store° the world they played for.　　85

But I do think it is their husbands' faults

If wives do fall. Say that they slack their duties

And pour our treasures into foreign laps;

Or else break out in peevish jealousies,

Throwing restraint upon us; or say they strike us,　　90

Or scant our former having in despite°—

70.　**troth:** truth.

72–73.　**joint-ring:** ring with two interlocking parts.

73.　**measures of lawn:** yards of fine linen.

74.　**exhibition:** payment.

85.　**store:** fill up.

91.　**scant . . . despite:** take away, out of spite, what they once gave.

Why, we have galls;° and though we have some grace,
Yet have we some revenge. Let husbands know
Their wives have sense like them. They see and smell
And have their palates both for sweet and sour,   95
As husbands have. What is it that they do
When they change° us for others? Is it sport?
I think it is. And doth affection° breed it?
I think it doth. Is't frailty that thus errs?
It is so too. And have not we affections?   100
Desires for sport? and frailty? as men have?
Then let them use us well; else let them know,
The ills we do, their ills instruct us so.°

Desdemona.

Good night, good night. Heaven me such uses° send,
Not to pick bad from bad, but by bad mend!°   105

Exeunt.

---

92. **galls:** senses of injury and insult.
97. **change:** exchange.
98. **affection:** desire; passion.
103. **instruct us so:** teach us to do the same.
104. **uses:** habits of thought.
105. **Not . . . mend:** not learn evil from seeing evil done but, by seeing evil, learn good from (or avoid) it.

Act V

Scene 1. *Cyprus. A street.*

Enter IAGO *and* RODERIGO.

Iago.
Here, stand behind this bulk;° straight will he come.
Wear thy good rapier bare,° and put it home.
Quick, quick! Fear nothing; I'll be at thy elbow.
It makes us, or it mars us; think on that,
And fix most firm thy resolution.   5

Roderigo.
Be near at hand; I may miscarry in't.

Iago.
Here, at thy hand. Be bold, and take thy stand.

Retires.

Roderigo.
I have no great devotion to the deed,
And yet he hath given me satisfying reasons.
'Tis but a man gone. Forth my sword! He dies!   10

Iago.
I have rubbed this young quat almost to the sense,°
And he grows angry. Now, whether he kill Cassio,
Or Cassio him, or each do kill the other,
Every way makes my gain. Live Roderigo,
He calls me to a restitution large   15
Of gold and jewels that I bobbed° from him

V.1.1. **bulk:** part of a shop or building projecting into the street.
   2. **rapier bare:** sword unsheathed.
  11. **quat . . . sense:** pimple (that is, Roderigo) nearly to the quick.
  16. **bobbed:** swindled.

As gifts to Desdemona.
It must not be. If Cassio do remain,
He hath a daily beauty in his life
That makes me ugly; and besides, the Moor   20
May unfold° me to him; there stand I in much peril.
No, he must die. But so, I hear him coming.

Enter CASSIO.

Roderigo.
I know his gait. 'Tis he. Villain, thou diest!

Makes a pass at CASSIO.

Cassio.
That thrust had been mine enemy indeed,
But that my coat° is better than thou know'st.   25
I will make proof° of thine.

Draws and wounds RODERIGO.

Roderigo.   O, I am slain!

IAGO *from behind wounds* CASSIO *in the leg and exits.*

Cassio.
I am maimed forever. Help, ho! Murder! Murder!

Enter OTHELLO.

Othello.
The voice of Cassio. Iago keeps his word.
Roderigo.
O, villain that I am!
Othello.   It is even so.
Cassio.
O help, ho! Light! A surgeon!   30

---

21. **unfold:** expose.
25. **coat:** either an outer coat (stronger than Roderigo expected) or an
    undergarment made of mail or another tough material.
26. **proof:** a test.

Othello.

'Tis he. O brave Iago, honest and just,

That hast such noble sense of thy friend's wrong!

Thou teachest me. Minion,° your dear lies dead,

And your unblest fate hies.° Strumpet, I come.

Forth of my heart those charms, thine eyes, are blotted.   35

Thy bed, lust-stained, shall with lust's blood be

    spotted.   [*Exit.*]

Enter LODOVICO *and* GRATIANO.

Cassio.

What, ho? No watch? No passage?° Murder! Murder!

Gratiano.

'Tis some mischance. The voice is very direful.

Cassio. O, help!

Lodovico. Hark!   40

Roderigo. O wretched villain!

Lodovico.

Two or three groan. 'Tis heavy° night.

These may be counterfeits. Let's think't unsafe

To come into° the cry without more help.

Roderigo.

Nobody come? Then shall I bleed to death.   45

Lodovico. Hark!

Enter IAGO *with a light.*

Gratiano.

Here's one comes in his shirt, with light and weapons.

Iago.

Who's there? Whose noise is this that cries on°

    murder?

---

33. **Minion:** hussy (that is, Desdemona).
34. **hies:** comes quickly.
37. **passage:** people passing by.
42. **heavy:** dark; gloomy.
44. **come into:** get closer to.
48. **cries on:** shouts or cries out.

Lodovico.

We do not know.

Iago.   Did not you hear a cry?

Cassio.

Here, here! For heaven's sake, help me!

Iago.   What's the matter?   50

Gratiano.

This is Othello's ancient, as I take it.

Lodovico.

The same indeed, a very valiant fellow.

Iago.

What are you here that cry so grievously?

Cassio.

Iago? O, I am spoiled,° undone by villains.

Give me some help.   55

Iago.

O me, lieutenant! What villains have done this?

Cassio.

I think that one of them is hereabout

And cannot make away.

Iago.   O treacherous villains!

To LODOVICO *and* GRATIANO.

What are you there? Come in, and give some help.

Roderigo.

O, help me there!   60

Cassio.

That's one of them.

Iago.   O murd'rous slave! O villain!

Stabs RODERIGO.

Roderigo.

O damned Iago! O inhuman dog!

Iago.

Kill men i' th' dark!—Where be these bloody

  thieves?—

---

54. **spoiled:** ruined; finished.

How silent is this town!—Ho! Murder! Murder!—
What may you be? Are you of good or evil?   65

Lodovico.

As you shall prove us, praise° us.

Iago. Signior Lodovico?

Lodovico. He, sir.

Iago.

I cry you mercy. Here's Cassio hurt by villains.

Gratiano. Cassio?   70

Iago. How is't, brother?

Cassio.

My leg is cut in two.

Iago.   Marry, heaven forbid!
Light, gentlemen; I'll bind it with my shirt.

Enter BIANCA.

Bianca.

What is the matter, ho? Who is't that cried?

Iago.

Who is't that cried?   75

Bianca.

O my dear Cassio! My sweet Cassio!
O Cassio, Cassio, Cassio!

Iago.

O notable strumpet!—Cassio, may you suspect
Who they should be that have thus mangled you?

Cassio. No.   80

Gratiano. I am sorry to find you thus. I have been to
seek you.

Iago.

Lend me a garter. So. O for a chair°
To bear him easily hence.

Bianca.

Alas, he faints! O Cassio, Cassio, Cassio!   85

---

66. **praise:** appraise; evaluate.
83. **chair:** stretcher.

Iago.

> Gentlemen all, I do suspect this trash
>
> To be a party in this injury.—
>
> Patience awhile, good Cassio.—Come, come.
>
> Lend me a light. Know we this face or no?
>
> Alas, my friend and my dear countryman   90
>
> Roderigo! No.—Yes, sure.—Yes, 'tis Roderigo!

Gratiano. What, of Venice?

Iago.

> Even he, sir. Did you know him?

Gratiano.   Know him? Ay.

Iago.

> Signior Gratiano? I cry your gentle pardon.
>
> These bloody accidents° must excuse my manners   95
>
> That so neglected you.

Gratiano.   I am glad to see you.

Iago.

> How do you, Cassio?—O, a chair, a chair!

Gratiano. Roderigo?

Iago.

> He, he, 'tis he. [*A chair is brought in.*] O, that's well
>   said;° the chair.
>
> Some good man bear him carefully from hence.   100
>
> I'll fetch the general's surgeon. [*To* BIANCA.] For
>   you, mistress,
>
> Save you your labor.° [*To* CASSIO.] He that lies slain
>   here, Cassio,
>
> Was my dear friend. What malice was between you?

Cassio.

> None in the world; nor do I know the man.

Iago. [*To* BIANCA.]

> What, look you pale?—O, bear him out o' th' air.   105

>   CASSIO *is borne off.*

---

95. **accidents:** events.
99. **said:** done.
102. **Save . . . labor:** never mind tending to Cassio.

Stay you, good gentlemen.—Look you pale, mistress?
Do you perceive the gastness° of her eye?
Nay, if you stare, we shall hear more anon.°
Behold her well; I pray you look upon her.
Do you see, gentlemen? Nay, guiltiness will speak,   110
Though tongues were out of use.

Enter EMILIA.

Emilia.

Alas, what is the matter? What is the matter, husband?

Iago.

Cassio hath here been set on in the dark
By Roderigo and fellows that are scaped.°
He's almost slain, and Roderigo quite dead.   115

Emilia.

Alas, good gentleman! Alas, good Cassio!

Iago.

This is the fruit of whoring. Prithee, Emilia,
Go know of° Cassio where he supped tonight.

To BIANCA.

What, do you shake at that?

Bianca.

He supped at my house; but I therefore shake not.   120

Iago.

O, did he so? I charge you go with me.

Emilia.

Oh fie upon thee, strumpet!

Bianca.

I am no strumpet, but of life as honest°
As you that thus abuse me.

Emilia.   As I? Fie upon thee!

---

107. **gastness:** terrified look.
108. **if . . . anon:** (probably) if you stay, we'll learn more soon.
114. **scaped:** escaped; on the loose.
118. **know of:** find out.
123. **honest:** chaste.

Iago.

  Kind gentlemen, let's go see poor Cassio dressed.°   125

To BIANCA.

  Come, mistress, you must tell's another tale.
  Emilia, run you to the citadel
  And tell my lord and lady what hath happed.
  Will you go on afore?

                              Exeunt all but IAGO.

                    This is the night
  That either makes me or fordoes me quite.°   [*Exit.*]   130

Scene 2. *A bedchamber in the castle;* DESDEMONA *in bed asleep, a light burning.*

Enter OTHELLO.

Othello.

  It is the cause,° it is the cause, my soul.
  Let me not name it to you, you chaste stars.
  It is the cause. Yet I'll not shed her blood,
  Nor scar that whiter skin of hers than snow,
  And smooth as monumental alabaster.   5
  Yet she must die, else she'll betray more men.
  Put out the light, and then put out the light.°
  If I quench thee, thou flaming minister,°
  I can again thy former light restore,

---

125. **Cassio dressed:** Cassio's wounds bandaged.
130. **fordoes me quite:** ruins me totally.
V.2.1. **It is the cause:** (Othello is reminding himself that Desdemona's
    supposed adultery is the reason he must execute her.)
  7. **Put . . . light:** Snuff out the candle, and then snuff out Desdemona's
    life.
  8. **flaming minister:** candle or lamp.

Should I repent me;° but once put out thy light,   10
Thou cunning'st pattern of excelling nature,
I know not where is that Promethean heat°
That can thy light relume.° When I have plucked
    the rose,
I cannot give it vital growth again;
It must needs wither. I'll smell it on the tree.   15

Kisses her.

O balmy breath, that dost almost persuade
Justice to break her sword. One more, one more!°
Be thus when thou art dead, and I will kill thee,
And love thee after. One more, and that's the last!
So sweet was ne'er so fatal. I must weep,   20
But they are cruel° tears. This sorrow's heavenly;
It strikes where it doth love. She wakes.

Desdemona.
Who's there? Othello?

Othello.   Ay, Desdemona.

Desdemona.
Will you come to bed, my lord?

Othello.
Have you prayed tonight, Desdemona?

Desdemona.   Ay, my lord.   25

Othello.
If you bethink yourself of any crime
Unreconciled as yet to heaven and grace,
Solicit° for it straight.°

Desdemona.
Alack, my lord, what do you mean by that?

---

10. **repent me:** regret my decision.
12. **Promethean heat:** divine flame. (In Greek mythology, the Titan
    Prometheus stole fire from heaven and gave it to humans.)
13. **relume:** relight.
17. **One more, one more!:** (Othello is kissing Desdemona.)
21. **cruel:** pitiless.
28. **Solicit:** petition; pray. **straight:** right away.

Othello.

> Well, do it, and be brief; I will walk by.°　　　　　　　30
> I would not kill thy unpreparèd spirit.
> No, heavens forfend! I would not kill thy soul.

Desdemona.

> Talk you of killing?

Othello. 　　　　　　Ay, I do.

Desdemona. 　　　　　　　　Then heaven

> Have mercy on me!

Othello. 　　　　　　Amen, with all my heart.

Desdemona.

> If you say so, I hope you will not kill me.　　　　　　35

Othello. Humh.

Desdemona.

> And yet I fear you; for you're fatal then
> When your eyes roll so. Why I should fear I know not,
> Since guiltiness I know not; but yet I feel I fear.

Othello.

> Think on thy sins.

Desdemona. 　　　　They are loves I bear to you.　　　40

Othello.

> Ay, and for that thou diest.

Desdemona.

> That death's unnatural that kills for loving.
> Alas, why gnaw you so your nether lip?
> Some bloody passion shakes your very frame.
> These are portents; but yet I hope, I hope,　　　　　45
> They do not point on° me.

Othello. 　　　　　　　　Peace, and be still.

Desdemona.

> I will so. What's the matter?

Othello.

> That handkerchief which I so loved and gave thee,
> Thou gav'st to Cassio.

---

30. **by:** nearby.
46. **point on:** point at (predict what will happen to).

Desdemona.   No, by my life and soul!
Send for the man, and ask him.
Othello.   Sweet soul, take heed,   50
Take heed of perjury; thou art on thy deathbed.
Desdemona.
Ay, but not yet to die.
Othello.   Presently.
Therefore confess thee freely of thy sin,
For to deny each article° with oath
Cannot remove nor choke the strong conception°   55
That I do groan withal. Thou art to die.
Desdemona.
Then Lord have mercy on me.
Othello.   I say, amen.
Desdemona.
And have you mercy too. I never did
Offend you in my life; never loved Cassio
But with such general warranty° of heaven   60
As I might love. I never gave him token.
Othello.
By heaven, I saw my handkerchief in's hand!
O perjured woman! thou dost stone° my heart,
And mak'st me call what I intend to do
A murder, which I thought a sacrifice.   65
I saw the handkerchief.
Desdemona.   He found it then.
I never gave it him. Send for him hither.
Let him confess a truth.
Othello.   He hath confessed.
Desdemona. What, my lord?

---

54. **article:** item (in the indictment for adultery—an example of Othello's
   extensive use of legal terminology in this scene).
55. **conception:** either belief in your guilt or the plan in my mind.
60. **warranty:** permission; sanction.
63. **stone:** harden; turn to stone.

Othello.

That he hath used° thee.

Desdemona.   How? unlawfully?

Othello.   Ay.   70

Desdemona.

He will not say so.

Othello.   No, his mouth is stopped.

Honest Iago hath ta'en order for't.°

Desdemona.

O, my fear interprets. What, is he dead?

Othello.

Had all his hairs been lives, my great revenge

Had stomach° for them all.   75

Desdemona.

Alas, he is betrayed, and I undone!

Othello.

Out, strumpet! Weep'st thou for him to my face?

Desdemona.

O, banish me, my lord, but kill me not!

Othello.

Down, strumpet!

Desdemona.

Kill me tomorrow; let me live tonight!   80

Othello.

Nay, if you strive—

Desdemona.

But half an hour!

Othello.   Being done, there is no pause.

Desdemona.

But while I say one prayer!

Othello.   It is too late.

Stifles her.

---

70. **used:** had sexual relations with.
72. **ta'en order for't:** arranged for it (Cassio's murder).
75. **stomach:** appetite; capacity.

Emilia. [*Within.*]

    My lord, my lord! What, ho! my lord, my lord!

Othello.

    What noise is this? Not dead? Not yet quite dead?   85

    I that am cruel am yet merciful;

    I would not have thee linger in thy pain.

    So, so.

Emilia. [*Within.*]

    What, ho! My lord, my lord!

Othello.   Who's there?

Emilia. [*Within.*]

    O, good my lord, I would speak a word with you.   90

Othello.

    Yes, 'tis Emilia.—By and by.—She's dead.—

    'Tis like she comes to speak of Cassio's death.

    The noise was high. Ha! No more moving?

    Still as the grave.—Shall she come in? Were't good?—

    I think she stirs again. No.—What's best to do?   95

    If she come in, she'll sure speak to my wife.

    My wife! My wife! What wife? I have no wife.

    O, insupportable! O heavy hour!

    Methinks it should be now a huge eclipse

    Of sun and moon, and that th' affrighted globe   100

    Should yawn at alteration.°

Emilia. [*Within.*]   I do beseech you

    That I may speak with you, O good my lord!

Othello.

    I had forgot thee. O, come in, Emilia.

    Soft, by and by.—Let me the curtains draw.—

Unlocks the door.

    Where art thou?

99–101. **Methinks ... alteration:** (Othello expresses the Elizabethan belief
    that nature reflects upheavals in human affairs.)

Enter EMILIA.

What's the matter with thee now?	105

Emilia.

O my good lord, yonder's foul murders done!

Othello. What? Now?

Emilia. But now, my lord.

Othello.

It is the very error° of the moon.

She comes more nearer earth than she was wont   110

And makes men mad.

Emilia.

Cassio, my lord, hath killed a young Venetian

Call'd Roderigo.

Othello.   Roderigo killed?

And Cassio killed?

Emilia.   No, Cassio is not killed.

Othello.

Not Cassio killed? Then murder's out of tune,   115

And sweet revenge grows harsh.

Desdemona.

O, falsely, falsely murdered!

Emilia.   O Lord! What cry is that?

Othello. That? What?

Emilia.

Out° and alas! that was my lady's voice.

Help! Help, ho! Help! O lady, speak again!   120

Sweet Desdemona! O sweet mistress, speak!

Desdemona.

A guiltless death I die.

Emilia.

O, who hath done this deed?

---

109. **error:** deviation from its course (another example of how natural
      disorder mimics, perhaps even causes, human disarray).
119. **Out:** (expression of sadness, intensifying "alas," which follows).

Desdemona.

    Nobody—I myself. Farewell.

    Commend me to my kind lord. O, farewell!   [*Dies.*]   125

Othello.

    Why, how should she be murd'red?

Emilia.   Alas, who knows?

Othello.

    You heard her say herself, it was not I.

Emilia.

    She said so. I must needs report the truth.

Othello.

    She's like a liar gone to burning hell!

    'Twas I that killed her.

Emilia.   O, the more angel she,   130

    And you the blacker devil!

Othello.

    She turned to folly, and she was a whore.

Emilia.

    Thou dost belie° her, and thou art a devil.

Othello.

    She was false as water.

Emilia.   Thou art rash as fire, to say

    That she was false. O, she was heavenly true!   135

Othello.

    Cassio did top her. Ask thy husband else.°

    O, I were damned beneath all depth in hell

    But that I did proceed upon just grounds

    To this extremity. Thy husband knew it all.

Emilia. My husband?   140

Othello. Thy husband.

Emilia.

    That she was false to wedlock?

---

133. **belie:** lie about; slander.

136. **else:** if you don't believe it.

Othello.

Ay, with Cassio. Had she been true,
If heaven would make me such another world
Of one entire and perfect chrysolite,°   145
I'd not have sold her for it.

Emilia.   My husband?

Othello.

Ay, 'twas he that told me on her first.
An honest man he is, and hates the slime
That sticks on filthy deeds.

Emilia.   My husband?

Othello.

What needs this iterance?° Woman, I say thy husband.   150

Emilia.

O mistress, villainy hath made mocks with love!
My husband say she was false?

Othello.   He, woman.

I say, thy husband. Dost understand the word?
My friend, thy husband; honest, honest Iago.

Emilia.

If he say so, may his pernicious soul   155
Rot half a grain a day! He lies to th' heart.
She was too fond of her most filthy bargain.

Othello. Hah?

Emilia.

Do thy worst.
This deed of thine is no more worthy heaven   160
Than thou wast worthy her.

Othello.   Peace, you were best.°

Emilia.

Thou hast not half that pow'r to do me harm
As I have to be hurt. O gull!° O dolt!
As ignorant as dirt! Thou hast done a deed—

---

145. **chrysolite:** topaz (a gemstone).
150. **iterance:** repetition.
161. **Peace . . . best:** It would be best to say no more.
163. **gull:** dupe; fool.

OTHELLO *moves to draw his sword.*

> I care not for thy sword; I'll make thee known,   165
> Though I lost twenty lives. Help! Help, ho! Help!
> The Moor hath killed my mistress! Murder! murder!

Enter MONTANO, GRATIANO, IAGO, *and* OTHERS.

Montano.
> What is the matter? How now, general?

Emilia.
> O, are you come, Iago? You have done well,
> That men must lay their murders on your neck.   170

Gratiano.
> What is the matter?

Emilia.
> Disprove this villain, if thou be'st a man.
> He says thou told'st him that his wife was false.
> I know thou didst not; thou'rt not such a villain.
> Speak, for my heart is full.   170

Iago.
> I told him what I thought, and told no more
> Than what he found himself was apt° and true.

Emilia.
> But did you ever tell him she was false?

Iago. I did.

Emilia.
> You told a lie, an odious, damnèd lie!   180
> Upon my soul, a lie! A wicked lie!
> She false with Cassio! Did you say with Cassio?

Iago.
> With Cassio, mistress. Go to, charm° your tongue.

Emilia.
> I will not charm my tongue; I am bound to speak:
> My mistress here lies murdered in her bed.   185

---

177.   apt: plausible; believable.
183.   charm: control; still (as with a magic spell).

All.

    O heavens forfend!

Emilia.

    And your reports have set the murder on.

Othello.

    Nay, stare not, masters. It is true indeed.

Gratiano.

    'Tis a strange truth.

Montano.

    O monstrous act!

Emilia.   Villainy, villainy, villainy!   190

    I think upon't—I think I smell't!—O villainy!

    I thought so then.—I'll kill myself for grief.—

    O villainy, villainy!

Iago.

    What, are you mad? I charge you get you home.

Emilia.

    Good gentlemen, let me have leave to speak.   195

    'Tis proper I obey him, but not now.

    Perchance, Iago, I will ne'er go home.

Othello.

    O! O! O!

Falls on the bed.

Emilia.   Nay, lay thee down and roar,

    For thou hast killed the sweetest innocent

    That e'er did lift up eye.°

Othello. [*Rising.*]   O, she was foul!   200

    I scarce did know you, uncle. There lies your niece,

    Whose breath, indeed, these hands have newly

        stopped.

    I know this act shows° horrible and grim.

Gratiano.

    Poor Desdemona! I am glad thy father's dead.

---

200. **lift up eye:** lift eyes to heaven (in purity of spirit).
203. **shows:** looks; seems.

Thy match was mortal to him, and pure grief   205
Shore° his old thread in twain. Did he live now,
This sight would make him do a desperate turn;°
Yea, curse his better angel from his side,
And fall to reprobation.°

Othello.

'Tis pitiful; but yet Iago knows   210
That she with Cassio hath the act of shame
A thousand times committed. Cassio confessed it;
And she did gratify his amorous works
With that recognizance° and pledge of love
Which I first gave her. I saw it in his hand.   215
It was a handkerchief, an antique token
My father gave my mother.

Emilia.

O God! O heavenly God!

Iago.

Zounds, hold your peace!

Emilia.   'Twill out, 'twill out! I peace?
No, I will speak as liberal as the north.°   220
Let heaven and men and devils, let them all,
All, all, cry shame against me, yet I'll speak.

Iago.

Be wise, and get you home.

Emilia.   I will not.

IAGO *offers to stab* EMILIA.

Gratiano.

Fie! Your sword upon a woman?

---

206. **Shore:** cut; sheared (an allusion to the Fates, who spin and then cut the thread of human life).

207. **turn:** act; deed.

209. **reprobation:** damnation. (If Brabantio had lived to see this murder, he would have killed himself, thus incurring damnation.)

214. **recognizance:** token; acknowledgment.

220. **liberal as the north:** freely as the north wind (blows).

Emilia.

    O thou dull Moor, that handkerchief thou speak'st of   225
    I found by fortune° and did give my husband;
    For often, with a solemn earnestness—
    More than indeed belonged to such a trifle—
    He begged of me to steal't.

Iago.   Villainous whore!

Emilia.

    She give it Cassio? No, alas! I found it,   230
    And I did give't my husband.

Iago.   Filth, thou liest!

Emilia.

    By heaven, I do not, I do not, gentlemen.
    O murd'rous coxcomb! What should such a fool
    Do with so good a wife?

Othello.   Are there no stones° in heaven
    But what serve for the thunder? Precious° villain!   235

Runs at IAGO *but is disarmed by* MONTANO. IAGO *stabs*
EMILIA.

Gratiano.

    The woman falls. Sure he hath killed his wife.

Emilia.

    Ay, ay. O, lay me by my mistress' side.

                          Exit IAGO.

Gratiano.

    He's gone, but his wife's killed.

Montano.

    'Tis a notorious villain. Take you this weapon,
    Which I have here recovered from the Moor.   240
    Come, guard the door without. Let him not pass,

---

226. **fortune:** chance.
234. **stones:** thunderbolts (to hurl at such a villain).
235. **Precious:** utter.

But kill him rather. I'll after that same villain,
For 'tis a damnèd slave.

               Exeunt all but OTHELLO *and* EMILIA.

Othello.   I am not valiant neither;
But ever puny whipster° gets my sword.
But why should honor outlive honesty?°   245
Let it go all.
Emilia.   What did thy song bode, lady?
Hark, canst thou hear me? I will play the swan,
And die in music. [*Singing.*] "Willow, willow,
    willow."
Moor, she was chaste. She loved thee, cruel Moor,
So come my soul to bliss, as I speak true.   250
So speaking as I think, alas, I die.   [*Dies.*]
Othello.
I have another weapon in this chamber;
It was a sword of Spain, the ice-brook's temper.°
O, here it is.—Uncle, I must come forth.
Gratiano. [*Within.*]
If thou attempt it, it will cost thee dear.   255
Thou hast no weapon, and perforce must suffer.
Othello.
Look in upon me then and speak with me,
Or, naked° as I am, I will assault thee.

Enter GRATIANO.

Gratiano.
What is the matter?
Othello.   Behold, I have a weapon;
A better never did itself sustain   260

---

244. **whipster:** contemptible fellow (ready to whip out his sword).
245. **honor outlive honesty:** reputation for bravery last longer than integrity.
253. **the ice-brook's temper:** tempered in ice-cold water.
258. **naked:** unarmed.

Upon a soldier's thigh. I have seen the day
That with this little arm and this good sword
I have made my way through more impediments
Than twenty times your stop.° But O vain boast!
Who can control his fate? 'Tis not so now.   265
Be not afraid, though you do see me weaponed.
Here is my journey's end, here is my butt,°
And very seamark of my utmost sail.°
Do you go back dismayed? 'Tis a lost° fear.
Man but a rush against Othello's breast,   270
And he retires.° Where should Othello go?
Now, how dost thou look now? O ill-starred wench!
Pale as thy smock! When we shall meet at compt,°
This look of thine will hurl my soul from heaven,
And fiends will snatch at it. Cold, cold, my girl?   275
Even like thy chastity.
O cursèd, cursèd slave!° Whip me, ye devils,
From the possession of° this heavenly sight!
Blow me about in winds! roast me in sulfur!
Wash me in steep-down gulfs of liquid fire!   280
O Desdemon! Dead Desdemon; dead. O! O!

Enter LODOVICO, MONTANO, CASSIO *carried in a chair, and*
OFFICERS *with* IAGO, *prisoner.*

Lodovico.
Where is this rash and most unfortunate man?
Othello.
That's he that was Othello? Here I am.

---

264. **stop:** power (to stop).
267. **butt:** goal; target (from archery).
268. **seamark . . . sail:** light marking my final destination.
269. **lost:** futile; wasted.
270–271. **Man but . . . retires:** Use only a reed to attack Othello's chest, and he will die.
273. **compt:** Judgment Day.
277. **cursèd slave:** (Othello is denouncing himself.)
278. **the possession of:** being possessed by.

Lodovico.

Where is that viper? Bring the villain forth.

Othello.

I look down towards his feet—but that's a fable.°   285

If that thou be'st a devil, I cannot kill thee.

Wounds IAGO.

Lodovico.

Wrench his sword from him.

OTHELLO *is disarmed.*

Iago.   I bleed, sir, but not killed.

Othello.

I am not sorry neither. I'd have thee live;

For in my sense, 'tis happiness to die.

Lodovico.

O thou Othello that was once so good,   290

Fall'n in the practice° of a cursèd slave,°

What shall be said to thee?

Othello.   Why, anything:

An honorable murderer, if you will;

For naught I did in hate, but all in honor.

Lodovico.

This wretch hath part confessed his villainy.   295

Did you and he consent in° Cassio's death?

Othello. Ay.

Cassio.

Dear general, I never gave you cause.

Othello.

I do believe it, and I ask your pardon.

Will you, I pray, demand that demi-devil   300

Why he hath thus ensnared my soul and body?

---

285. **that's a fable:** (Othello is referring to the belief that the Devil has
cloven, or split, hoofs.)

291. **in the practice:** through the plotting or machinations. **slave:** villain.

296. **consent in:** agree to; plan.

Iago.

    Demand me nothing. What you know, you know.

    From this time forth I never will speak word.

Lodovico.

    What, not to pray?

Gratiano.   Torments° will ope your lips.

Othello.

    Well, thou dost best.   305

Lodovico.

    Sir, you shall understand what hath befall'n,

    Which, as I think, you know not. Here is a letter

    Found in the pocket of the slain Roderigo;

    And here another. The one of them imports

    The death of Cassio to be undertook   310

    By Roderigo.

Othello.

    O villain!

Cassio.   Most heathenish and most gross!

Lodovico.

    Now here's another discontented paper°

    Found in his pocket too; and this, it seems,

    Roderigo meant t' have sent this damnèd villain;   315

    But that, belike,° Iago in the interim

    Came in and satisfied him.°

Othello.   O thou pernicious caitiff!

    How came you, Cassio, by that handkerchief

    That was my wife's?

Cassio.   I found it in my chamber;

    And he himself confessed it but even now   320

    That there he dropped it for a special purpose

    Which wrought to his desire.°

Othello.   O Fool! Fool! Fool!

---

304. **Torments:** torture.
313. **discontented paper:** letter expressing discontent or resentment.
316. **belike:** most likely.
317. **satisfied him:** gave him a satisfactory explanation.
322. **wrought to his desire:** was designed to achieve what he wished.

Cassio.

There is besides in Roderigo's letter,
How he upbraids Iago, that he made him
Brave° me upon the watch; whereon it came   325
That I was cast;° and even but now he spake,
After long seeming dead—Iago hurt him,
Iago set him on.

Lodovico.

You must forsake this room and go with us.
Your power and your command is taken off,   330
And Cassio rules in Cyprus. For this slave,
If there be any cunning cruelty
That can torment him much and hold him long,°
It shall be his. You shall close prisoner rest°
Till that the nature of your fault be known   335
To the Venetian state. Come, bring him away.

Othello.

Soft you,° a word or two before you go.
I have done the state some service, and they know't.
No more of that. I pray you, in your letters,
When you shall these unlucky° deeds relate,   340
Speak of me as I am. Nothing extenuate,
Nor set down aught in malice. Then must you speak
Of one that loved not wisely but too well;
Of one not easily jealous but, being wrought,°
Perplexed° in the extreme; of one whose hand,   345
Like the base Judean,° threw a pearl away
Richer than all his tribe; of one whose subdued° eyes,

---

325. **Brave:** incite; provoke.
326. **cast:** fired; dismissed.
333. **hold him long:** keep him alive (while being tortured).
334. **close prisoner rest:** remain a prisoner.
337. **Soft you:** wait.
340. **unlucky:** unfortunate.
344. **wrought:** used; worked upon.
345. **Perplexed:** upset; disturbed.
346. **Judean:** (a Biblical reference, to Judas's betrayal of Jesus).
347. **subdued:** crying.

Albeit unusèd to the melting mood,
Drops tears as fast as the Arabian trees
Their med'cinal gum.° Set you down this.   350
And say besides that in Aleppo° once,
Where a malignant and a turbaned Turk
Beat a Venetian and traduced the state,
I took by th' throat the circumcisèd dog
And smote him—thus.   355

Stabs himself.

Lodovico.
O bloody period!°
Gratiano.   All that is spoke is marred.
Othello.
I kissed thee ere I killed thee. No way but this,
Killing myself, to die upon a kiss.

Falls on the bed and dies.

Cassio.
This did I fear, but thought he had no weapon;
For he was great of heart.
Lodovico. [*To* IAGO.]   O Spartan dog,   360
More fell° than anguish, hunger, or the sea!
Look on the tragic loading of this bed.
This is thy work. The object poisons sight;
Let it be hid.° [*Bed curtains are drawn.*] Gratiano, keep°
      the house,
And seize upon the fortunes° of the Moor,   365

---

350. **med'cinal gum:** resin from myrrh trees.
351. **Aleppo:** (city once part of Turkey and now in Syria).
356. **period:** end; conclusion.
361. **fell:** pitiless; cruel.
364. **Let it be hid:** (Draw the bed curtains to hide the bodies.) **keep:** stay in.
365. **seize upon the fortunes:** take legal possession of the goods.

For they succeed on you.° To you, lord governor,°
Remains the censure° of this hellish villain,
The time, the place, the torture. O, enforce it!
Myself will straight aboard, and to the state
This heavy act with heavy heart relate.   370

Exeunt.

---

366. **succeed on you:** pass on to you as by inheritance. **lord governor:**
(that is, Cassio).
367. **censure:** trial and punishment.

A Dramatic Monologue

The Laboratory
Ancien Régime
Robert Browning

*Robert Browning (1812–1889), an English poet, is known
for his dramatic monologues, in which a speaker who is
not the poet addresses a listener who doesn't speak. The
subtitle of this monologue indicates that it takes place in
France during the "old regime," before the Revolution of
1789. By the end of this chilling speech, what do you
know about the psychology of the speaker?*

1

Now that I, tying thy glass mask tightly,
May gaze thro' these faint smokes curling whitely,
As thou pliest thy trade in this devil's-smithy—
Which is the poison to poison her, prithee?

2

He is with her, and they know that I know   5
Where they are, what they do: they believe my tears flow
While they laugh, laugh at me, at me fled to the drear
Empty church, to pray God in, for them!—I am here.

3

Grind away, moisten and mash up thy paste,
Pound at thy powder—I am not in haste!   10
Better sit thus, and observe thy strange things,
Than go where men wait me and dance at the King's.°

---

12. the King's: This is probably a reference to Louis XIV, king of France from
   1643 to 1715. A number of people at Louis's court killed enemies by
   poisoning them.

4

That in the mortar—you call it a gum?
Ah, the brave tree whence such gold oozings come!
And yonder soft phial,° the exquisite blue,   15
Sure to taste sweetly, is that poison too?

5

Had I but all of them, thee and thy treasures,
What a wild crowd of invisible pleasures!
To carry pure death in an earring, a casket,
A signet,° a fan-mount, a filigree° basket!   20

6

Soon, at the King's, a mere lozenge to give,
And Pauline should have just thirty minutes to live!
But to light a pastile,° and Elise, with her head
And her breast and her arms and her hands, should drop dead!

7

Quick—is it finished? The color's too grim!   25
Why not soft like the phial's, enticing and dim?
Let it brighten her drink, let her turn it and stir,
And try it and taste, ere she fix and prefer!

8

What a drop! She's not little, no minion° like me!
That's why she ensnared him: this never will free   30
The soul from those masculine eyes—say, "no!"
To that pulse's magnificent come-and-go.

---

15. phial (fī′ əl): small glass bottle.
20. signet: seal (sometimes mounted on a ring) used to mark documents as
official; the mark itself. **filigree:** lacelike ornamental work usually made of
intertwined wire of gold or silver.
23. pastile (pas·tēl′): here, pellet of aromatic paste, burned for fumigating or
deodorizing.
29. minion: delicate person.

9

For only last night, as they whispered, I brought
My own eyes to bear on her so, that I thought
Could I keep them one half minute fixed, she would fall   35
Shriveled; she fell not; yet this does it all!

10

Not that I bid you spare her the pain;
Let death be felt and the proof remain:
Brand, burn up, bite into its grace—
He is sure to remember her dying face!   40

11

Is it done? Take my mask off! Nay, be not morose;
It kills her, and this prevents seeing it close:
The delicate droplet, my whole fortune's fee!
If it hurts her, beside, can it ever hurt me?

12

Now, take all my jewels, gorge gold to your fill,   45
You may kiss me, old man, on my mouth if you will!
But brush this dust off me, lest horror it brings
Ere I know it—next moment I dance at the King's!

On Playing Othello
Sir Laurence Olivier Interviewed by Kenneth Tynan

Sir Laurence Olivier (1907–1989) was one of the most versatile and highly regarded English stage and film actors of his time. Kenneth Tynan (1927–1980) was an influential critic and social commentator.

Kenneth Tynan: *What was there in your conception of the part that made it different from the conventional Othellos that we're used to seeing?*

Sir Laurence Olivier: Well, you know that very rough estimate of the theme of Shakespearean tragedy. It's constantly said that Shakespearean tragedy is founded by Shakespeare upon the theme of a perfect statue of a man, a perfect statue; and he shows one fissure in the statue, and how that fissure makes the statue crumble and disappear into utter disorder. From that idea you get that Othello is perfect except that he's too easily jealous; that Macbeth is perfect except that he's too ambitious; that Lear is perfect except that he's too bloody-minded, too pigheaded; that Coriolanus is too proud; that Hamlet lacks resolution; and so on. But there seems to me, and there has grown in me a conviction over the last few years, that in most of the characters, not all, but in most of them, that weakness is accompanied by the weakness of self-deception, as a companion fault to whatever fault may be specified by the character in the play. It's quite easy to find in Othello, and once you've found it I think you have to go along with it; that he sees himself as this noble creature. It's so easy in the Senate scene for you to present the absolutely coldblooded man who doesn't even worry about marital relations with his wife on his honeymoon night, to reassure the Senate that he's utterly perfect, pure beyond any reproach as to his character, and you can find that, and trace it, constantly throughout. He's constantly wishing to present himself in a certain light, even at the end, which is remarkable. I believe, and I've tried to show, that when he says "not easily jealous" it's the most appalling bit of self-deception. He's the most easily jealous man that anybody's ever written about. The minute he suspects, or thinks he has the smallest grounds for suspecting, Desdemona, he wishes to think her guilty, he wishes to. And the very first thing he does, almost on top of that, is to give way to the passion, perhaps the worst temptation in the world, which is murder. He immediately wants to murder her, immediately. Therefore he's an extremely hotblooded individual, an extremely savage creature who has kidded himself and managed to kid everybody else, all this time, that he's nothing of the kind. And if you've got that, I think you've really got the basis of the character. . . .

Tynan: *There is also a sense of a caged animal in your performance. . . . Are you conscious of [the] power you have over audiences—and over other actors, for that matter?*

Olivier: I'm not very conscious of the workings of it. I feel consciousness of the desirability of having that ingredient in my work, very much so. *Othello,* of course, screams for it. It's the only play in the whole of Shakespeare in which a man kills a woman [onstage], and if Shakespeare gets an idea he goes all out for it; . . . he doesn't pull any punches. As an alchemist Shakespeare gets hold of that one, all right. Therefore, if you feel that thing in yourself, that sort of easily released or closely guarded animal inside you, you must use it in this part, of all parts.

A News Feature

After Four Centuries, Shakespeare Comes to Life in His Natural Habitat
Alan Riding

LONDON, June 8—So finally, almost four centuries later, the prologue to *Henry V* seemed to make sense as Mark Rylance, the actor playing King Harry of England, stood at the front of the stage in the replica of Shakespeare's Globe Theater and asked: "Can this cockpit hold the vasty fields of France? Or may we cram within this wooden O the very casques that did affright the air at Agincourt?"

Still, if in Shakespeare's time the answer was no doubt affirmative, today Mr. Rylance, who is also director of the new Globe Theater, might well have added a few questions. Can this cockpit become more than an Elizabethan theme park? Will this new wooden O offer a genuine theater experience or merely a fresh stopover on the Shakespearean tourist circuit?

The dream of building a replica of Shakespeare's Globe Theater near its original site beside the Thames was born of the American actor Sam Wanamaker as far back as 1970. But in the long years of fund-raising and construction that followed, there was ample time for Londoners to sound skeptical. Now, with the Globe finally completed and its first full season underway, the verdict is in. Both public and critics have been won over.

Mr. Wanamaker died in 1993, but his daughter, the actress Zoë Wanamaker, will herself recite the prologue to *Henry V* at the start of a special performance called "Triumphes and Mirth" to be attended by Queen Elizabeth on Thursday. The evening, which will include Act IV of *Henry V* and Act V of *The Winter's Tale,* will mark the official opening of the theater.

Preview performances open to the public nonetheless began late last month, offering an occasion to judge both the quality of the productions and the experience of reliving something of the ambience of popular English theater at the turn of the seventeenth century. In August two non-Shakespearean plays of the era will take over: Thomas Middleton's comedy *A Chaste Maid in Cheapside* and *The Maid's Tragedy* by Francis Beaumont and John Fletcher.

Of the first two plays to be performed in repertory, *Henry V* seems to fare best. This production, directed by Richard Olivier, seeks as far as possible to show the play as it might have been performed at the original Globe, using ornate period costumes and an all-male cast (even for the roles of Mistress Quickly and Katherine).

In contrast to its depiction in epic movie versions of the play or even some theater productions on large stages, the Battle of Agincourt takes place largely out of view. But flag waving, battle sounds, and military drums echoing from the musicians' gallery behind the stage suffice to create the right mood. By doubling up roles, the fifteen actors, including the Americans Christian Camargo and Steven Skybell, handle the play's thirty-six characters.

The production connects well with the audience—the five hundred "groundlings" in the "bear pit" and the nine hundred others sitting on wooden benches in three galleries—by presenting the play with the patriotic fervor that Shakespeare intended. Thus, if the new Globe's hope is to provoke interaction between stage and public as in times of yore, it proved easy to incite pantomimic boos and hisses whenever the enemy French appeared. Yet this did not detract from the high drama and earthy humor of the play itself.

Mr. Rylance's Henry was well received. "He is a superb Shakespearean, with an engagingly hesitant manner that invites us into his mind," Robert Butler wrote in *The Independent* on Sunday. "He suggests again and again that he has reached a crossroads and that his next thought could go either way. In this lovely, intimate theater, he finds a stillness and poise."

The Winter's Tale proved more of a challenge simply because, by passing successively through tragedy, magic, humor, and romance, it lacks the clear narrative drive of *Henry V.* In this case, with the stage covered in earth, the director David Freeman has opted for a more modern rendering of the play, with the Sicilians and Bohemians dressed respectively in brown and blue peasant tunics, rubber tires serving as prop chairs, and Autolycus the rogue appearing boozily in raincoat and trilby, with bottle in hand.

With Mark Lewis Jones playing Leontes, king of Sicily, the production does succeed in achieving high poignancy at its climactic end, when Leontes' much-offended Queen Hermione appears as a statue and comes back to life. "She's warm," the king cries out. In this case, women play women's roles, with Anna-Livia Ryan warmly applauded for her strong performance as Perdita, Leontes' daughter.

Yet almost as important as the productions is the novelty of attending a play in this theater, modeled on the first Globe, which was built in 1599 and destroyed by fire in 1613. Its replacement was closed by the Puritans in 1642. Like its predecessors, the new Globe is made of wood, with Norfolk reeds providing the thatched roof and lime plaster covering the walls. The stage and galleries are covered, but the "bear pit" is open to the skies.

So, yes, the weather is an important variable, above all for the groundlings, who are not allowed to block the view of others by sheltering under umbrellas. And yes, it has rained during some recent performances, prompting some groundlings to try to find shelter and others to ignore the elements in fairly heroic manner. But *The Winter's Tale,* with its frequent references to stormy weather, added some laughs. "The skies look grimly and threaten present blusters," one character warned as rain began to fall one recent evening.

The acoustics, which were tested in a series of workshops in 1995 and in a "prologue season" in 1996 that included a production of *The Two Gentlemen of Verona,* are better than expected, considering that, with public galleries covering three quarters of the wooden O, actors must inevitably turn their backs to some of the audience. Forgetting stormy skies and aching legs, the groundlings, who can stand within feet of the performers, are best positioned.

Extraneous noise like the occasional passing aircraft poses no serious problem. Perhaps more disturbing for audiences used to sitting in the dark of a theater looking at a lighted stage is that, even at night under subtly located floodlights, the entire wooden O is visible, including actors, audience, and theater staff members wandering among the groundlings offering wine or sandwiches during the performance.

It could be argued that in Shakespeare's day the Globe was anything but solemn. In fact, some commercialism reflects the fact that the new Globe is meant to be financially self-sufficient and that it must still raise $25 million in order to complete the $60 million complex planned for this site. The hope is that a new indoor Inigo Jones Theater, an education center, and an exhibition area will be ready for inauguration on September 21, 1999, the four hundredth anniversary of the opening of the first Globe.

For the moment, though, the Globe has passed its first test of offering a new experience to theatergoers. Indeed, even when the novelty wears off, it should still be able to present theater in a different way. "They are talking to you, asking you questions, involving you in their fears," Benedict Nightingale wrote enthusiastically of the performers in *The Times* of London. "At the Globe you too are part of the debate. Isn't that what theater is all about?"

—from *The New York Times,*
June 12, 1997

Troubled Othellos: Life Imitates Art

Over the centuries, art and life have curiously merged for actors playing Othello.

Edmund Kean is one of the greatest Othellos in theatrical history. Kean was savagely attacked by the press and the public in 1825, however, when he was sued for adultery by Alderman Cox, a minor London politician whose wife had a long affair with Kean. Kean first became acquainted with Mrs. Cox when she fainted with emotion during the fourth act of *Othello.* The performance was halted and she was carried across the stage to Kean's dressing room.

Eight years later Kean was found guilty of adultery and was fined. The next time he stepped onto the stage in the role of Othello, the audience, incited by the press, became enraged at a man guilty of adultery (in his private life) accusing an innocent woman (a character in a play) of the same crime.

Although not a line of the play could be heard above the jeers and hisses, Kean bravely stayed onstage to the end. Afterward he addressed the audience, stating that he stood before them "the representative of Shakespeare's heroes" and would not "submit to be trampled upon by a hostile press" but would leave the stage for good if the public demanded it. The audience replied with cries of "No, no! Kean forever!"

But Kean never fully recovered from this ordeal. The quality of his performances declined, and he sometimes would mix details of his private life into the lines of the character he was playing. On March 25, 1833, in the role of Othello, he faltered at the line "Villain, be sure thou prove my love a whore" and collapsed into the arms of his son Charles, who was playing Iago. Kean was carried from the stage and died several weeks later.

The personal life of the American actor Edwin Forrest tragically mirrored his emotionally charged portrayal of Othello. In 1848, Forrest discovered that his wife had been unfaithful, and he sued for divorce. In the ensuing trial the evidence was so manipulated that Forrest himself was found guilty of adultery and forced to pay alimony. For eighteen years he sought and failed to have this judgment reversed. The only outlet for his anguish was his acting. According to Norman Sanders, as Othello Forrest "alternated the extraordinary power of his rages with a tender affectionateness, which became in the last act a self-pitying wavering between desire for revenge and longing for a lost love that apparently characterized his own life."

Perhaps inspired by the stories of Kean and Forrest, Ruth Gordon and Garson Kanin wrote a script about an actor playing Othello who so identifies with his character that he becomes insanely jealous of his actress wife, who is playing Desdemona. In 1947, George Cukor directed the film *A Double Life*, which was based on the script, and Ronald Coleman won an Academy Award for his performance as the actor who could not separate himself from his part.

A Critical Comment

Iago's Diseased Intellectual Activity
William Hazlitt

William Hazlitt (1778–1830) was an influential English essayist and critic. He is noted for his brilliant mind and his direct and unpretentious writing style. His analysis of Iago is reprinted here as it originally appeared.

Some persons, more nice than wise, have thought this whole character unnatural, because his villainy is *without a sufficient motive.* Shakespear, who was as good a philosopher as he was a poet, thought otherwise. He knew that the love of power, which is another name for the love of mischief, is natural to man. He would know this as well or better than if it had been demonstrated to him by a logical diagram, merely from seeing children paddle in the dirt or kill flies for sport. Iago in fact belongs to a class of character, common to Shakespear and at the same time peculiar to him; whose heads are as acute and active as their hearts are hard and callous. Iago is to be sure an extreme instance of the kind; that is to say, of diseased intellectual activity, with the most perfect indifference to moral good or evil, or rather with a decided preference of the latter, because it falls more readily in with his favourite propensity [and] gives greater zest to his thoughts and scope to his actions. He is quite or nearly as indifferent to his own fate as to that of others; he runs all risks for a trifling and doubtful advantage; and is himself the dupe and victim of his ruling passion—an insatiable craving after action of the most difficult and dangerous kind. "Our ancient" is a philosopher, who fancies that a lie that kills has more point in it than an alliteration or an antithesis; who thinks a fatal experiment on the peace of a family a better thing than watching the palpitations in the heart of a flea in a microscope; who plots the ruin of his friends as an exercise for his ingenuity, and stabs men in the dark to prevent *ennui*. His gaiety, such as it is, arises from the success of his treachery; his ease from the torture he has inflicted on others. He is an amateur of tragedy in real life; and instead of employing his invention on imaginary characters, or long-forgotten incidents, he takes the bolder and more desperate course of getting up his plot at home, casts the principal parts among his nearest friends and connections, and rehearses it in downright earnest, with steady nerves and unabated resolution.

—from *Characters of Shakespear's Plays* (1817)

A Critical Comment

Self-Knowledge at a Terrible Price
David Bevington

David Bevington is a contemporary American Shakespeare scholar and critic.

As a tragic hero, Othello obtains self-knowledge at a terrible price. He knows finally that what he has destroyed was ineffably good. The discovery is too late for him to make amends, and he dies by his own hand as atonement. The deaths of Othello and Desdemona are, in their separate ways, equally devastating: He is in part the victim of racism, though he nobly refuses to deny his own culpability, and she is the victim of sexism, lapsing sadly into the stereotypical role of passive and silent sufferer that has been demanded of her. Despite the loss, however, Othello's reaffirmation of faith in Desdemona's goodness undoes what the devil-like Iago had most hoped to achieve: the separation of Othello from a belief in goodness. In this important sense, Othello's self-knowledge is cathartic and a compensation for the terrible price he has paid. The very existence of a person as good as Desdemona gives the lie to Iago's creed that everyone has his or her price. She is the sacrificial victim who must die for Othello's loss of faith and, by dying, rekindle that faith. . . . She cannot restore him to himself, for self-hatred has done its ugly work, but she is the means by which he understands at last the [imaginary] and wantonly destructive nature of his jealousy. His greatness appears in his acknowledgment of this truth, and in the heroic struggle with which he has confronted an inner darkness we all share.

—from Introduction to *Othello* by William Shakespeare (1988)

A Critical Comment

The Tragedy of Othello
Mark Van Doren

Mark Van Doren (1894–1972) was a noted American critic, poet, and university teacher.

The evil in *Othello* is more than an atmosphere. It is a force, and its origin, like the origin of everything else in the tragedy, is the character of the hero. Othello is both the best and the worst of men; he is both superior to passion and its slave. That is why his career can develop into tragedy. . . . To speak only of Othello's deception by Iago, and of the accidents, the misunderstandings, the coincidences which make this deception work smoothly, is to overemphasize the mechanics of the catastrophe; or it is not to see them all. The superb machinery of *Othello* shows us more than a man whom various tricks of external fate combine in an awful moment to render pitiful. There is the pity of it, but there is also the terror. Othello is a great and fearful man; one who generates his own tragic atmosphere as he goes. . . . The precarious balance in his nature between the monstrous and the tender, the giant and the lover, the soldier and the man, is a balance of powers no one of which can be denied its reality. Add the conflict in him between the past and the present, the remote and the local, the free and the confined; add once again his genius for extending and expressing himself in the whole atmosphere of the world at whose center he moves; and it will be seen that he deserves his tragedy. It is both his punishment and his privilege: his punishment, because in the permanent order of things dimensions like his must be reduced; his privilege, because they are his dimensions and his alone.

—from *Shakespeare* (1939)